HAWAI'I SpOOKY TALES 5

MORE TRUE LOCAL SPINE-TINGLERS

COLLECTED BY
RICK CARROLL

THE
BESS
PRESS

3565 Harding Ave, Honolulu, Hawai'i 96816
(808) 734-7159 fax (808) 732-3627 www.besspress.com

Design: Carol Colbath
Moon logo from a design by Kevin Hand
Cover photograph: Thomas N. Colbath

Library of Congress Cataloging-in-Publication Data

Carroll, Rick
    Hawaii's best spooky tales 5 : more true local
spine-tinglers / collected by Rick Carroll.
        p.   cm.
    ISBN 1-57306-130-1
    1. Ghost stories, American – Hawaii.
2. Tales – Hawaii.   3. Legends – Hawaii.
I. Title.
GR580.H3.C374 2001   398.25-dc20

The prayer to an *'aumaukua*, on page 53, is from Pukui, Mary Kawena, and

Samuel H. Elbert. *Hawaiian Dictionary*. Rev. and enlarged ed. Honolulu:

University of Hawai'i Press, 1986.

Printed in the United States of America

For Shannon, Chip, Cole, and

Shane Allen Tillett (b. April 27, 2001)

Contents

Hawai'i's Best Spooky Tales: The Original (2000; originally published in 1996 under a different title)

Danny Akaka, Akoni Akana, Martha Beckwith, Burl Burlingame, Emme Tomimbang Burns, Ed Chang, Don Chapman, Lei-Ann Stender Durant, Leslie Ann Hayashi, James D. Houston, Mark Allen Howard, Phil Helfrich, Steve Heller, Nicholas Love, Bernard G. Mendonca, Gordon Morse, Victoria Nelson, Rob Pacheco, Mary Kawena Pukui, Nanette Purnell, Lee Quarnstrom, Pam Soderberg

Hawai'i's Best Spooky Tales (1997)

Jay Agustin, Rich Asprec, Keala Binz, Cynthia Broc, Catherine Chandler, Micah Curimao, Nancy K. Davis, Darlynn D. Donahue, Helen Fujie, George Y. Fujita, Richard S. Fukushima, Bernard D. Gomes, Jeff Hitchcock, Ashley Kahahane, Hapa Koloi, Eugene Le Beaux, Tania Leslie, Linda Liddell, Alberta H. Lindsay, Jerrica Ann Keanuhea Lum, Sandy Martino, Gordon Morse, Gladys K. Nakahara, Lisa Okada, Lana T. Paiva, Kaui Philpotts, Mary Kawena Pukui, Kim-Erin Riley, Nicole Sarsona, Ed Sheehan, Ron Terry, Allen B. Tillett, Sr., Maureen Trevenen, Scott Whitney, Jason Wong, Dennis G. Yanos

Hawai'i's Best Spooky Tales 2 (1998)

Andrea Hunt Bills, Carolyn Sugiyama Classen, Thomas N. Colbath, Amanda Fahselt, Madelyn Horner Fern, Camie Foster, Helen Fujie, Nyla Fujii-Babb, Richard S. Fukushima, George Fuller, Joyce Garnes, Jeff Gere, Babs Harrison, Jerry and Debby Kermode, Alexis Cheong Linder, Ben Lowenthal, Ruben (Lopina) Makua, Chandelle Rego-Koerte, Stephanie Kaluahine Reid, Doug Self, Pam Soderberg, Shirley Streshinsky, Crystal Tamayose, Aaron Teves, Pat Leilani Young

Hawai'i's Best Spooky Tales 3 (1999)

Reggie K. Bello, Hannah J. Bernard, Suzan Gray Bianco, Robert W. Bone, Sonny Kaukini Bradley, Marcie Carroll, Carolyn Sugiyama Classen, Mary Ann Collignon, Maria de Leon, Ann Donahue, John Flinn, Nyla Fujii-Babb, Richard S. Fukushima, Steve Heller, Michael Hocker, Nicole Howe, Jachin Hsu, Claire Ikehara, Van Love, Charles Kauluwehi ("Uncle Charlie") Maxwell Sr., Simon Nasario, Kaui Philpotts, Michael Sturrock, Robert S. Tripp, Brian and Gigi Valley, Joana McIntyre Varawa, Robert Wenkam

Hawai'i's Best Spooky Tales 4 (2000)

Dominic Kealoha Aki, Kamaka Brown, Reney Ching, Dion-Magrit Coschigano, Angela Dollar, Lani Donovan, Aja Dudley, Pua Lilia DuFour, William Ellis, Joyce Guzman, Germaine Halualani-Hee, Kenneth Makaio Hee, James D. Houston, Margo Howlett, Ronson Kamalii, Francis Morgan, Simon Nasario, Rob Pacheco, Lee Quarnstrom, Susan Scott, Brad Smith, Gloriana C. Valera, Sunny Young

Hawai'i's Best Spooky Tales 5 (2001)

Noelle Barbosa, Kalina Chang, Michael Dalke, Bill Daugherty, Cheryl Duarte, Keoni Farias, Woody Fern, Joyce Guzman, Fox Harmon, Sam Henderson, Margo Howlett, Kelly S. Hunsicker, Leona Kalua, Myron "Skip" Kawakami, Robert E. Landsman, Healani Ortiz, Charlene Peters, Keao Rawlins, Scottie Shelton, David Soares, Paula and Wayne Sterling, Yu Shing Ting, Al Tolentino, Kathy Tretsven, Dayle Turner, Gloriana C. Valera

Acknowledgments

Mahalo nui loa to

All who buy, borrow, and read these books

Hawai'i librarians, who keep my books under lock and key

Young readers of Hawai'i, who ask,
"When's the next book coming out?"

Buddy and Revé and Jeela and Tina and Lori and Rob at Bess Press

Carol Colbath, who designs the spookiest covers

All who are present and those who are not.

All stand now, please, and take a bow.

(It's okay, we know you're there.)

Rick Carroll

About Rick Carroll

Rick Carroll is the creator of the best-selling Hawai'i's Best Spooky Tales series, collections of true, first-person stories of mysterious encounters in the Hawaiian Islands today. Carroll began collecting oral histories in Hawai'i two decades ago; he has brought more than 150 new local authors to print in his Spooky Tales books.

Hawai'i's Best Spooky Tales 5 is Carroll's sixth collection of spooky tales; his first was *Chicken Skin: True Spooky Stories of Hawai'i*, reprinted as *Hawai'i's Best Spooky Tales: The Original.*

He shares the stories at schools, libraries, bookstores, and conferences, including O'ahu's annual Talk Story Festival, and this year he will host Outrigger Waikiki's first Spooky Tales Festival, featuring twenty of his contributing authors.

His spooky stories have appeared in West Coast newspapers, national magazines, and television, including The Travel Channel. He is the only local storyteller to be a Visiting Artist on Lāna'i at the Lodge at Kō'ele.

Carroll is the author of numerous Hawai'i books, including *Hawai'i: True Stories of the Island Spirit* (Travelers' Tales, San Francisco). His book *Huahine: Island of the Lost Canoe*, will be published in late 2001.

He lives in old Ka'a'awa in windward O'ahu, near Lae o ka 'Ō'io, which translates either to "the point of the bone fish" or ('Oi'o) "the point of the night marchers."

Introduction

"Beneath those stars is a universe of gliding monsters."
—Herman Melville

"Ninety-eight percent of Hawai'i's spooky stories are *shibai*," Jim Bartels, former curator of 'Iolani Palace, told me one day at Bestsellers bookstore in downtown Honolulu, where he was buying a *Star-Bulletin*.

"I know, Jim, the other two percent are in my books."

The point was made.

His and mine.

If you want the usual Hawai'i ghost stories everyone knows, please look elsewhere. If you want the top two percent of Hawai'i's true, spooky stories, look no further.

You will read about the headless horseman of Sand Island, hide-and-go-seek in coffins, a Maui boy's night marcher encounter, purloined beads that haunt a man even today, Madame Pele's rare Waikīkī appearance, Oscar, the ghost who hangs out in a Pearl City dentist's office, the inside story on a haunted house on O'ahu's River Street, the car-stopping spirit of Kamehameha Highway, the perils of pig hunters, and much more.

If you think these stories are *shibai*, tell it to Scottie Shelton, the contributing author of "A *Malihini*'s First Impressions." "I'm glad my year-and-a-half of tears, screams, and all-around sheer terror will turn into a good story for your book," she told me. "I especially hope that the mainland haoles who move over will think twice before they take lightly the spooky stories of our islands.

Nothing like a good haunting to give you a different perspective and renewed respect!"

WHY HAWAI'I'S BEST SPOOKY TALES GIVE YOU CHICKEN SKIN

Truth is always stranger than fiction.

And Hawai'i's Best Spooky Tales are true stories that really happened to real people right here in Hawai'i.

For a story to appear in Hawai'i's Best Spooky Tales, its author must sign a publication agreement stating the story is true.

Many stories are two-sourced, i. e., witnessed by two or more people, a test not even most daily journalists bother to meet today.

Not every story submitted makes it to print. I read and hear more than a hundred stories a year. Only a few pass my test. The test is simple: each story must give me chicken skin. I must get a visceral reaction to the written words. My hair stands on end. I feel that tingle of excitement up and down my spine. I shiver and grab my elbows.

Those that meet my test are sent to The Bess Press. Together, we choose the best for publication. Each year since 1995, we've selected the best true spooky stories for your reading pleasure. I am pleased once again to present you with the latest collection.

HOW DO I GET ALL THOSE STORIES?

People ask, "How do you get all those stories?" They just come to me, I tell them. It's true. Sometimes I can look at people and know they've got a good, spooky story. The method may be intuitive, but it's never failed yet.

I'll give you three examples.

At Windward Mall for a haircut one afternoon, I looked in the mirror and saw myself and stylist Fox Harmon, all dressed in black. She told me when she looks in her grandmother's "Dark Mirror" she sees other people who really aren't there. I asked her to write the story and she did. It's on page 32.

With hours to kill before my flight to San Francisco, I decided to get a shine on my new shoes at Honolulu International Airport. Al Tolentino (he's the shoeshine man), soon had me in stitches with his spooky tales from "small keed" time. Tolentino makes his literary debut here with five hair-raising stories in "Old Kaka‘ako." See page 91.

For several years I've asked master storyteller Woody Fern to contribute a story. I knew he grew up in Ka‘a‘awa, a very spooky place. He always promised but never delivered until one dark night in Wahiawā, when he appeared at a reading at the library with his manuscript in hand. I am excited to offer you his story, "Uncle Eddie," a reminiscence of Friday nights at Honey's house in old Ka‘a‘awa, where everything was wonderful except the long, dark ride home from the country. Go to page 47.

SPOOKY PREVIEW AHEAD

You're still here? I haven't scared you away?
Good. Now, here's a spooky preview.

One of my favorite windward O'ahu storytellers is Margo Howlett, who contributed "The Good News Dog" to *Hawai'i's Best Spooky Tales 4*. She returns here now with "Tūtū Lady's Taro Patch," about meeting a woman who will make you scream.

No stranger to the pages of Hawai'i's Best Spooky Tales, Joyce Guzman, a Kaua'i-born storyteller now living in Southern California, presents "Hunting Kalalau," a scary memoir about her father.

Oh, yes, I discovered Ms. Guzman while surfing the Net.

Come on, admit it, it's always a little spooky going to the dentist. Well, wait 'til you read Dr. Myron "Skip" Kawakami's story about "Oscar."

You're driving home alone around midnight. You see a hitchhiker on the road to Hilo. Would you stop? You won't after reading Cheryl Duarte's "The Hitchhiker of Laupāhoehoe."

If ghosts haunt Waikīkī, nobody talks about it. I guess they're afraid to scare tourists. That's why I was surprised to hear—and delighted to share—David Soares's story about the night "Madame Pele Visited Waikīkī."

Sitting all alone on a dark, empty beach on Maui, waiting for his father who's fishing, a little boy feels, but can't see, something walking by. Whatever it is, it kicks sand on him. Keoni Farias describes one of the scariest nights of his life in "Just Them, Passing Through."

START GRADUALLY WITH *"PUEO* TALES"

Now that your hair's standing up, you may want to start gradually with *"Pueo* Tales," three spooky tales that illustrate what a remarkable bird the Hawaiian owl really is, although maybe only on Kaua'i. In "A *Pueo* Blessing," Paula and Wayne Sterling follow an owl home over cane haul roads from Wilcox Memorial Hospital on the day their daughter is born. Kathy Tretsven describes one dark night all alone on the narrow, winding road to Kōke'e in "A *Pueo* Saved My Life." "A Historic Encounter" describes how owls twice saved the life of Kaua'i pioneer Valdemar Knudsen.

One of my favorite stories is a piece of investigative journalism. *Midweek* reporter Yu Shing Ting set out to debunk the Pele myth and after interviewing park rangers and Pele victims reached the only sensible conclusion: "Leave the Rocks Alone."

Here's more of what you will find inside:

• When a parade comes down your street, it's really exciting. When you look again and the parade has disappeared, it's really scary. Noelle Barbosa gives an eyewitness account of what she saw, and didn't see, in "The Procession."

• You never know whom you'll meet on the Big Island, as Kalina Chang explains in "A Lady's Advice." Ms. Chang also contributed "Drums in the Night," about Israel Kamakawiwo'ole, and "*Kolohe* Spirits," which may help explain why things go bump in the night in Hawai'i.

• Sometimes it's easy to see Madame Pele's work. Other times, it's a nightmare. Michael Dalke describes the night he and three pals got "No Sleep in Pele's World."

• Thousands of motorists daily drive by O'ahu's Red Hill, little realizing it's haunted by not one ghost but maybe twenty or more, as Bill Daugherty reveals in "The Spirits of Red Hill."

• When Robert E. Landsman was a boy growing up in Mānoa Valley he removed beads from a Koʻolau burial cave and found his life full of misfortune; he reveals the awful details of a painful haunting in "The Purloined Beads."

• Sam Henderson and a lady friend go for a beach walk in Waimānalo on a full-moon June night and discover they are not alone in "Moonlight Stroll in Waimānalo."

• Visit ʻIolani Palace, and you may see more than meets the eye. In her account, Kelly S. Hunsicker describes what happened to her on "A Full Moon Friday the Thirteenth."

• Even *akamai* Island-born pig hunters can stray into *kapu* zones on the hunt. As proof, I offer "Pig Hunters on Sacred Grounds," by Leona Kalua, wife of veteran pig hunter Al Kalua.

• Healani Ortiz and pals go to Waimānalo Carnival one night. They take turns taking pictures of each other wearing devil's horns—and discover "Something's in the Picture."

• Some people have supernatural powers. Charlene Peters describes the eerie events on a full-moon night in Kailua when "A Hopi Elder Meets a Hawaiian *Kahuna*."

• Keao Rawlins describes a house on Oʻahu's River Street haunted by human relics the frightened tenants found in "The Screaming Pouch."

• Dayle Turner, a professor of English at Leeward Community College, likes to hike alone. One day he's followed by a curious canine known as "The Spirit Dog of Kokokahi."

• Gloriana C. Valera describes two related experiences with aging parents in "The Last *Aloha* and Farewell."

• On the other hand, Scottie Shelton's story, "A *Malihini*'s First Impressions" makes you wonder if everyone's favorite tropical paradise isn't sometimes Hell on Earth.

Finally, if you think Haleakalā crater is extinct, you've been misinformed. The crater is very much alive and way overdue to go off again, something to consider when you join me on Maui for a "Ride to the Source."

BEYOND THE REEF

Hawai'i's Best Spooky Tales are scaring more people everywhere. The books have been featured on the Travel Channel three times, and individual tales have been reprinted in national magazines and West Coast newspapers, on the World Wide Web, and in *Travelers' Tales Hawai'i* (O'Reilly & Associates, San Francisco, available in bookstores nationally and at travelerstales.com).

Can't wait for the next Spooky book? Check out my column, now appearing on Hawaii Road Runner at http://www.hawaii.rr.com/leisure/reviews/rick_carroll/

Wherever you go, whatever you do, be *akamai*.

Rick Carroll
Honolulu, Hawai'i

Hauntings

Shortly after a Honolulu couple moved into their new house, strange, supernatural incidents began to occur. Then, they caught a mystery flu no doctor could cure. They decided to abandon the house, and on the day they moved they found . . .

The Screaming Pouch

This is a story my grandmother told me. It happened in the late fifties when she and my grandfather were still living on Oʻahu. Two good friends of theirs had just bought a house, I think near River Street, and after they moved in, strange things started to happen—the typical stuff, doors slamming when there's no wind, windows opening and closing—and then they started getting sick.

They went to the doctor, and the doctor could never find anything wrong. They called in a priest to bless the house, and they thought everything was okay after that, but they started getting sick again—flu, fever, nausea, stomachaches, and headaches. Strange things started happening again.

They asked a Hawaiian *kahuna* to come and bless the place and he did, and they thought everything was okay again, but then it all started happening again.

Eventually, they just couldn't take it. They bought another house and began moving out. As my grandparents were helping them clean out the house, they found a little pouch, not much bigger than a little hand purse, stuffed all the way up in the corner of one of the closets, stuffed way back so no one could see it when they were just looking in the closet.

When they opened the pouch and looked inside, they found human hair and fingernails—not clippings, but actual fingernails ripped off a hand—and human teeth, and some other things, I don't remember exactly what. They thought it was so odd for those things to be in there.

So they were burning rubbish out in the front yard—back then it was still legal to do that—and they threw the pouch in. As soon as it caught fire, they heard a piercing human scream, coming from the pouch, coming from the fire.

After they moved out, they had a *kahuna* come back to check out the place, and he said he couldn't find anything wrong with the house—no bad vibes. And nothing ever happened to them in their new house, no problems, no more getting sick, no more doors slamming.

Whatever it was, it all had to do with the pouch. Nobody knows who put the pouch there or why. I've read about things like that used in New Orleans for voodoo magic, they're called juju pouches, or something like that. They put things like human hair and fingernails and teeth in the pouch, and they use it for various reasons. There are different ones to attract wealth and good luck and everything, but this was one of the bad ones.

Keao Rawlins was born and raised in Hawai'i and spent most of his life on the Big Island. His grandfather, George, was a World War II veteran, and his grandmother, Betty, was the daughter of a Japanese immigrant. He now lives on O'ahu with his wife, Zenelle, and his daughter, Zena.

If you drive by O‘ahu's Red Hill at sundown, keep an eye out for the headless horseman. Or the ghosts of seventeen men who forever are known as . . .

The Spirits of Red Hill

One of Hawai'i's major landmarks, Red Hill Fuel Facility, is haunted by the ghosts of men killed during construction of this unique underground fuel depot. Seventeen men were killed, one every two months. Two drowned in a tank, others from falls, cave-ins, electrocution, and asphyxiation. One got pulled into a conveyor belt. Another failed to stop for a marine sentry.

The massive subterranean facility is a system of twenty vertical tunnels drilled in a ridge of volcanic rock between Moanalua and Hālawa valleys four miles on the 'Ewa side of Pearl Harbor. The tanks, which are 175 feet below grade, are singular in size and location. They are 250 feet high—that's 25 stories—and 100 feet in diameter. You could put two Aloha Towers—it's only 10 stories tall—in each tank and have lots of room leftover.

Each tank holds 12.6 million gallons of fuel oil, jet fuel, aviation gasoline, and diesel fuel. A series of pumps, valves, and pipelines connects the tanks to Pearl Harbor's Hotel Pier and Hickam Air Force Base. Two tunnels, upper and lower, access the tanks. The upper tunnel has a small railway, nicknamed "The Howling Owl" because of its eerie sound effects. The lower tunnel was used to haul out construction rubble.

Nearly three thousand men worked on the project from December 26, 1940, to September 28, 1943, with only two days off, both on Christmas Day.

The job cost $43 million and was completed nine months ahead of schedule—not bad for an idea drawn on a cocktail napkin at the Halekūlani by James Growden, a young hydraulics engineer, for the contractor, Morrison-Knudsen. One of the most remarkable engineering feats of World War II, the mammoth fuel depot is a National Historic Civil Engineering Landmark.

I recently took a tour of the Red Hill Underground Fuel Storage Facility, and although I didn't see anything supernatural, I did learn about its spooks. Red Hill's dark, musty tunnels are filled with spirits. According to *The Center Relay* newsletter, many workers sense unseen presences in the tunnels, and some have reported eerie encounters. One worker, who doesn't believe in the supernatural, described his experience, which occurred in the deepest part of the tunnel, in a story entitled "Strangers in the Night: Fuel Ghouls, Oil Gargoyles, and Petro-dactyls."

"I was doing maintenance work at the sump pit," he recounted, "when suddenly a strange feeling of uneasiness swept over me. My hair stood on end and my blood ran cold. I couldn't see anyone or anything, yet someone was there.

"I edged away from the pit, and the feeling eased. Not believing in a spiritual world, I was puzzled by this, and after a few minutes I returned to the pit.

"Again I was assailed by a strange sense of foreboding. The hair rose on my back and arms. I knew someone was there.

"I hurried away, leaving my work undone. Just before my shift ended, I returned. Whatever it was, it had gone, and I proceeded to finish the job."

In another eerie encounter, a control room worker saw someone walking away down the tunnel. He knew no one should be there. The stranger turned and saw him and raised his arm, beckoning the worker to come down to him.

"No, you come here," the worker said.

The silent figure again raised his arm, beckoning the worker.

"No, you come," the worker shouted, uneasy about finding an unknown intruder 450 feet underground.

The mystery stranger beckoned again and again before he disappeared into the gloomy tunnel.

The tunnels of Red Hill are haunted not only by the ghosts of construction workers, but also by a headless horseman who appeared often at the turn of the century before last. His appearance is documented in "The Legend of Red Hill Hollow," found in the May 1, 1943, edition of the *Red Hill Weekly*.

In the late 1800s, the Red Hill site was known as Pukake Hill, and travelers on horseback often encountered a headless horseman on a white steed. The rider always appeared on the 'Aiea side of the hill as the sun began to "gray the skies," and "as long as he kept behind a traveler there was no need to worry; however, death would strike in the families of those whom the horseman passed."

The headless horseman of Red Hill was seen by many people up until 1900 in and around 'Aiea. As you pass Red Hill while homeward bound in the evening commute, you may want to keep an eye out.

Born in Central Pennsylvania, Bill Daugherty is a graduate of the Pennsylvania State University and Capitol Bible Seminary in Lanham, Maryland. Bill and his wife, Clara, have lived in beautiful windward O'ahu for over almost three years.

When strange things start
happening in your new
home, you probably should
get the house blessed right
away by a Hawaiian *kahuna*,
or spiritual advisor of your
choice. If strange things keep
happening, you can blame
the cats, or . . .

Kolohe *Spirits*

We used to live 'Ewa Beach side. When development just became too much, we moved windward. This was in 1992. At the time, our daughter was distraught and did not want to move; she said she had nightmares about this place, and that if we moved there something bad would happen. And she was right. My mother passed away after we made an offer on the house.

We moved anyway, and had the house properly blessed. We told our daughter nothing bad was going to happen just because we moved. So far, this has been true, but there are strange goings-on from time to time, and mostly they happen to me.

The first thing happened one night when I wanted to tape something that was going to be on TV. I put a tape into the VCR. The program was not going to be on for another fifteen minutes, so I was looking at a book. I was alone at the time. As I sat there in the quiet, the videotape ejected from the machine. The remote was on the table, and nothing was near it. I didn't think too much of that— no big deal that the tape ejected. In a few minutes I could go put it back in.

Well, about five minutes later, the tape went back into

the VCR. Now this was a different story. You may be able to eject the tape without touching the machine, but to put it back in, you have to manually push it.

I told a friend, and he said, "Ah, you just have *kolohe* spirits there, no need worry."

So I don't, despite several other occasions when unexplainable little things happened, such as being in bed (our bedrooms are on the bottom floor) and hearing a radio turn on upstairs, not always the same radio, and sometimes it's the VCR. I just go up and turn it off.

Twice now, a flashlight I keep in the computer room turned on, once while I was walking by in the dark.

My cats are not capable of doing any of these things, as some of my friends have suggested; they always blame cats.

I awoke in the middle of the night a couple of months ago to the smell of Maui Rain, the perfume. It was very strong and distinct. I went back to sleep eventually and when I awoke later and got up, the smell was still lingering, but faintly.

I have no problem living with these incidents, as there seems to be no malice involved. I asked an old man who has lived in the area since the forties if he knew of any burials nearby. He said he didn't. I plan to research the ancient history of this immediate area, as soon as I get a chance.

Kalina Chang is a graphic artist who lives in windward Oʻahu. She paddles with Keahiakahoe Canoe Club, in Kahaluʻu, and enjoys writing and crafts. She is currently editing and doing cover art for a mainland author.

If you visit a dentist in a certain Pearl City building you may get more than your teeth straightened; it could be the hair on your head. Dr. Myron "Skip" Kawakami explains all in his story about . . .

Oscar

After several years in Seattle, in 1985 I decided to come back to Hawai'i and practice dentistry in Honolulu. I found an office in Pearl City on Ka'ahumanu Street, which, as you know, is named for a Hawaiian queen, and, well, basically, I took over the lease from another doctor who was in the process of moving. After the other fellow moved out we started remodeling. One day he stopped by, looked in the door, and said, "Hey, Skip, did you get this place blessed?"

"Oh, no, why?" I asked.

"You'll find out later," he said.

I asked some of the other fellows in the building about it, and they said there's a spirit called Oscar in the building. So I told the guys, okay fine.

And right away I kind of felt, well, there are good spirits and there are bad spirits. And being as I kind of felt good about it, I decided Oscar must be a good spirit. Come to find out, Oscar is what is called a *wadabuzo*, which in Japanese means somebody who's playful with water.

We had the place blessed as people normally do any-time they start a new business, and I told the fellow who was blessing the place about the possible spirit. I said I had no qualms about it because from what I understood, it's a good spirit.

Anyway, everything was okay for a while.

The first incident, well, we always had problems with the water, but I never thought about it. It's just dentistry, I thought.

Then a fellow opened up his new office across the hall, and one night someone forget to turn off the dental evacuation system. A little wooden wedge or something got stuck in the vacuum and kept a valve open and flooded his suite and everyone downstairs.

We laughed about it. We said, "Well, Oscar was getting his last hurrah." But ever since then, we've all heard doors open and shut and slam and nobody's there. I always leave my door open.

Weird things happen, nothing bad, nothing sinister, often friendly. I like to fish, and once I went to Lahaina Jackpot and my gals called and said, "Doc, have you been thinking about the office?"

"Yes, a little bit," I said. "Why?"

They said that when they came to the office that morning the chairs—usually we put our chairs back the same way when we leave every day—were in the position they would be in if I had been working that morning.

The other thing that's kind of interesting: whenever I am on vacation, or when I am gone for some other reason, the phone doesn't seem to ring; it's as if everybody knows I'm gone, enjoying myself. There's no activity, Oscar doesn't seem to hang around, and when I come back things seem to pick up again. It's almost as if he's kind of attached to me. I feel that he likes to be in my company, be there when I'm there.

One of our staff members, who's worked for fourteen years, and followed me from one office to another, believes in spirits, and she told me, "You know, Oscar's actually a female." And I laughed and said, "I don't know!"

He, or she, is kind of friendly, and we always think of Oscar. When we had the blessing, we put out a bottle of gin for my dad and some Kahlúa for Oscar, just assuming that's what he likes. It was just the thought.

We've had our share of leaks—I mean every kind of imaginable leak—and you know, in dentistry, we use a lot of water. We've had leaks in the rinsing bowl, the evacuation systems, the hand-piece system, the auto-developer for the X-rays. We replaced everything with new over the years and still have problems.

Working alone at night, I've never really been bothered by him—or her. Oscar's never scared anybody. So far, patients have never experienced Oscar, but I suppose it could happen, if a person had the right mind. You know, some people can sense certain things. I know at times I have had feelings that something will happen and it happens—the phone will ring and it does. That type of thing. I'm not a real religious person, but I do believe there is something that helps determine, or has a play in making things happen.

You know, some people didn't want Oscar here. There used to be a Japanese religious group, up on the third floor, that believed in spiritual healing, and they would walk around this place chanting, marching up and down the stairs, trying to make Oscar go away. I told them, "Hey, don't chase away Oscar," and they said, "Huh?" and they got really, really defensive.

We don't know why Oscar is here, but we found out that the owners of the building are actually a *hui* known as Oceanview Cemetery Ltd. I guess at one time, long ago, this was an old Hawaiian burial place.

People may say that all of these things are coincidental, but I truly believe there are signs in this world that lead you one way or the other. Oscar means no harm, just wants to be here and share the space. Basically it's peaceful coexistence, that's what it is.

Dr. Myron "Skip" Kawakami is a Pearl City dentist, decorated Vietnam veteran (he won the Bronze Star), and noted sport fisherman who once caught a Big Island marlin worth $25,000 in the Lahaina Jackpot Tournament. A native of Hawai'i, Kawakami studied dentistry at the University of Washington and practiced in Seattle for many years before returning home to Hawai'i.

Full Moon

A Hopi Elder Meets a Hawaiian Kahuna

A Full Moon Friday the Thirteenth

Moonlight Stroll in Waimānalo

When the moon is full in Hawai'i anything can—and usually does—happen. Cars leave the road. People see things that aren't there. Grown men pull the covers over their head. The extraordinary becomes routine. But nobody ever could have guessed what would happen in Kailua on a full moon night when . . .

A Hopi Elder Meets a Hawaiian Kahuna

It was a full moon night on an equinox. A friend from Arizona named Roy Little Sun was visiting me in Kailua. He is a Hopi elder and shaman. We had been doing some healing of the meridians and lei lines of the *heiau* in the Kawai Nui marsh area. At the stone quarry we built a huge medicine wheel with a local Hawaiian *kahuna*. A metaphysical cultural exchange, if you will. The wheel is still at the quarry pit by the visitor's lookout. It looks like a mini-Stonehenge.

We had all heard the story about an old *kahuna* named Daddy Bray of the Rainbow Energy, who connected to the Hopis in the 1950s. He found out that both the Hawaiians and the Hopis have the same sacred chants, and that the Hopis sent out their shamans hundreds of years ago to find an island that was their brother and realized that it was Hawai'i.

Well, that night we had a big spiritual gathering at my home in Kailua with the Hopi shaman and the Hawaiian *kahuna*, and various spiritual healers and teachers from around the Islands, and my very dear friend Arthur, who is a well-known medium and psychic in Honolulu. Arthur was late—which was unusual for him—because he could not find his rings and the bracelet he always wears when he goes out.

We all gathered and prayed and chanted in Hopi and Hawaiian and, all of a sudden, it started to pour rain outside—I mean really hard and fast and loud—and the wind whipped up. Roy took his staff and thumped it three times on the floor and—just like that—there was loud thunder and lightning and we all felt like we were in another realm and then it was all over: peaceful and calm.

Arthur looked down at his hand and saw that his lost rings were on his fingers and the missing bracelet was around his wrist. His son, Adam, also wore a bracelet that night, but when he looked down it was cut in half and on the floor.

Nobody knew what that meant, only that some peculiar force had manifested itself that night in Kailua when the Hopi elder and Hawaiian *kahuna* got together. We each had a story to tell, but I always thought this was the best.

Charlene Peters has lived in Hawai'i off and on since she was seven years old. She now lives in Kailua, where she is involved in Hawaiian and Native American Indian spiritual activities.

It was the right time and the right place. Two adventurous young women go to 'Iolani Palace (they'd heard stories about spirits and things nobody can explain) to see what, if anything, happens there on . . .

A Full Moon Friday the Thirteenth

Kelli and I are the best of friends, like sisters in a past life who met in the here and now. Both of us share a love for and deep curiosity about all things supernatural. She was here from the mainland for a visit after just having left Hawai'i in June. Well, as luck would have it, her stay included a Friday the thirteenth, and even better, there was a full moon on that night!

After hearing several stories about 'Iolani Palace and other nearby sites that are haunted, we decided, being the adventurous types we are, that a full-moon Friday the thirteenth would be the best night to go see for ourselves. So hopping into the car around 10:30 P.M., we made the drive from Schofield Barracks to Honolulu. Along the way there was rain that turned into downpours, but that didn't stop us. By the time we reached the palace it had stopped raining. It was a warm tropical night with a nice breeze blowing. The full moon lit up the night quite brightly.

Walking down Punchbowl Street, we decided to go see the Royal Mausoleum nearby. Kings are buried there, and we have heard tales of night marchers who sometimes end their walks right on that very spot, so we thought it a good idea to check it out. By this time it was nearly 11:30, and although we did get some eerie feelings that gave us chicken skin, we didn't see or hear anything out of the ordinary.

But 'Iolani Palace—that was a different story. As we made our way to the palace, Kelli and I joked a bit, I think to help alleviate whatever fear we both felt but didn't want to make real by talking about.

All I could do was look at the palace and then look away, because I had this feeling that there was something there I didn't like. What it was I couldn't put my finger on, but it was there all the same.

Kelli, on the other hand, had entered the palace grounds through the iron gate. I timidly followed her. It was the oddest thing. Inside the gate, it was pitch black, so dark the palace was barely visible. The only reason we knew it was there was because of the lights on the building. And there was no breeze, no sound, NOTHING! That right there was enough to scare us. We stayed a little longer. All of a sudden I saw a figure in one of the uppermost windows! And just as I was turning to tell Kelli it was time for us to get out of there, she turned to me and said, "Let's get out of here! It's time to go!"

As we left the grounds and stepped out onto the public sidewalk, we were bombarded with light and noise and heard the last three strikes of midnight. After calming down some, I asked Kelli why she was so ready to leave the grounds. She said, "As I stood there inside the gates I felt a cold breeze pass through me and the hairs on the back of my neck stood up!" I felt her arm and, for sure, she had chicken skin, and that's when I got it too.

By the time we made it all the way back to Schofield, my husband, Todd, was already in bed, sound asleep, so we had to wait until morning to tell him what had happened to us. He humored us by listening and seemed interested, although I know him better than that; he doesn't really believe in things that go bump in the night. We had planned on an evening out in Waikīkī and Honolulu, so we asked him if he could go with us to ʻIolani Palace.

"Why? You guys were already there last night," he said.

We told him we'd feel safer if he was with us, and this way maybe we'd get to see a little more than the previous night.

We all went to dinner and then stopped off at a favorite night spot for a quick drink. Then it was on to the palace again! And let me tell you: What a difference between this and the night before! The moon was still quite full, and when we went in we could actually see. We felt the breeze, we heard the street noise, everything. It was a totally different place. And yes, once again it was midnight, only this time we heard all twelve strikes. Kelli had her camera with her, so she had Todd take pictures of us in front of the palace steps. She took pictures of those big trees, the burial mound on the grounds, all sorts of things she found of interest. After that we decided to call it a night and headed back up the island. Kelli's camera still had some pictures left on it, so she used those up and went to get the film developed at a one-hour photo place. Needless to say we were anxious to see the pictures of 'Iolani Palace, and wouldn't you know—only one came out! It was the very first picture—of her and me by the steps—and we could see a figure that looked like an old Hawaiian warrior, and he was on the very top step right behind us.

Kelly S. Hunsicker is a military spouse, living at Schofield Barracks. She works as an outdoor recreation assistant. She and her husband moved to O'ahu in January 1999.

On a full-moon night,
a Hawaiian musician and a
lady friend go for a beach
walk and discover they are
not alone on their . . .

Moonlight Stroll in Waimānalo

It was a balmy summer night, I'd say about June of 1997, and a lady friend and I were about to have a stroll down the beach at Waimānalo. It was a beautiful full moon night, and the stars were out, so we parked our car on Laumilo Street, which runs parallel to the beach and Kalaniana'ole Highway, and took one of the pathways to get down to the beach.

I'd say the path was a good ninety feet long, bordered on both sides by houses. On the Kailua side were *milo* bushes, and on the Makapu'u side, mock orange and a wooden fence, about six feet high.

We were about twenty-five feet down the path, headed to the beach, with another ten to fifteen yards to go before we had open space to the beach. And it got very chilly all of a sudden. My friend clenched my elbow and pointed. I looked up, and about five feet in front of us was a looming shadow at least a foot-and-a-half, maybe two feet, taller than I, with broad shoulders. It didn't totally obscure the path, but it was very big. Its shoulders were twice as wide as mine, and it must have been at least seven-and-a-half feet tall. I didn't discern a face. It was just a very big shadow, and it was humanoid.

It just stopped and we froze. And knowing a little bit about Hawaiian culture, we prostrated ourselves, noses in the sand. All we felt was cold—not cool, cold—air brush over our shoulders, and we stayed down there pretty shook-up for a while before we looked at each other and decided it was safe to stand up.

We didn't dare turn around. We walked down to the beach. We turned right and walked to the beach park and took the long way back to the car.

Hawaiian activist and musician Sam Henderson teaches ukulele and slack key guitar. Other local musicians he has performed with include Moe Keale, Darrel Lupenui, and Frank Hewett.

Companions

When Fox Harmon was a little girl, her grandmother told her she had "the gift." She didn't fully understand what her grandmother meant until she inherited . . .

The Dark Mirror

It's a dark mirror. I am looking at it now. The glass of the mirror itself has a dark cast to it, but sometimes it seems dark in other ways. It is surrounded by an ornate, gold-carved frame. There once was a ribbon that lined the inside edge of the frame, but what remains are only moth-eaten shreds—a reminder of what used to be.

Not only is the mirror large, but it is heavy as well. I have no idea of its age; there are no hints or clues.

I am looking at it now.

The mirror has always held me spellbound, for it was my grandmother's before I inherited it. She was a small Filipino woman with what she called "the gift." She told me I've inherited that gift as well and, in time, would come to accept it fully.

I guess to her it seemed logical to bestow me with the mirror, one of the few belongings she brought with her from the Philippines. It hung in my grandmother's living room, and when I was a little girl it frightened and fascinated me. My mother said I had an overactive imagination. My grandmother clucked that she just didn't understand.

My grandmother said faces sometimes appeared in the mirror. Whose faces I do not know. When they came, strange things happened in my grandmother's house. She knew the faces and what could happen when they appeared. Sometimes, when the mean woman showed herself, doors opened and slammed shut and things were pushed from shelves. Another face belonged to a beautiful woman, richly dressed, and she seemed to enjoy making coffee cups rattle and clank together on their hooks behind closed cupboard doors.

As a child I never witnessed any of the faces or experienced the events. I only heard about them from my grandmother or from my parents, who always claimed there were logical explanations for such episodes. They didn't believe in my grandmother's mirror.

I would stand in front of the mirror for hours, hoping to see for myself, yet poised for flight if anything appeared.

A peculiar habit my grandmother had was to turn the mirror to face the wall at night before she went to bed. She never said why; she just did it.

My grandmother died at seventy-eight. She caught a cold while visiting us when we lived in Seattle, and she died the next day. Now, I've got the mirror. My granddad gave it to me twelve years after my grandmother's passing. He said she wanted me to have it.

I hung my grandmother's mirror in my bathroom. I looked at the mirror every day but didn't see anything. And then it happened.

I've seen two faces. I think the first was the beautiful rich woman from an earlier time. I was brushing my teeth and as I turned to leave the bathroom I caught the reflection out of the corner of my eye. Our gazes locked. She smiled and vanished. I was left standing there, staring at my own reflection.

The second incident happened two days later. I walked into the bathroom looking for a hairbrush that sits in a basket below the mirror. The face that materialized was my grandmother's.

I don't know how long it was before I could catch my breath. It seemed stuck in my throat. She smiled and she mouthed the words, "Don't forget."

I think I nodded, because she nodded in return before she was gone. I knew what she meant without having to say more. I turned the mirror before going to bed that night, as I do every night now.

Fox Harmon, who lives in Kailua on Oʻahu's windward side, is a wife and the mother of an eleven-year-old son who loves spooky tales. She grew up in Seattle, and worked as a youth counselor in Philadelphia before making a major life change. She moved to Hawaiʻi, where she now works as a hairstylist. She enjoys dabbling in writing and keeping an eye on her grandmother's dark mirror, which continues to present a cast of mysterious characters.

If you go hiking alone in
Hawai'i, it's always a good
idea to let someone know
where you're going, and
when you plan to return,
because out there on the
trail, you may encounter a
lot more than nature, as
Dayle Turner discovered
the day he met . . .

The Spirit Dog of Kokokahi

While hiking in the spring of 1996 on the windward side of O'ahu, I had an encounter with a friendly yet mysterious dog. At the time, not far from my home in Kāne'ohe I'd discovered a new trail with a starting point off Kāne'ohe Bay Drive *mauka* of the Kokokahi YWCA.

After scouting out the route one afternoon, I returned at noon the next day to do some trail maintenance and exploring. While I parked my car in a small pullout by the trailhead, I noticed a rather large German shepherd sniffing around the hedges nearby. When I opened the door of my vehicle to get out, the amiable pooch, a handsome brown-and-black animal, trotted over and made himself available for a pet and how-d'ya-do.

Thinking the dog would head off down the street to wherever his home was, I shouldered my pack and started up the trail. After no more than ten yards, I could hear my new friend bounding after me. Not wanting company, I stopped and tried to shoo him back toward the road, but he'd have none of that.

Instead, as I windmilled my arms while repeating "Go home" a half-dozen times, he just sat on his haunches, his head tilted slightly to the left, his eyes gazing curiously. Realizing the futility of my shooing efforts, I decided to plod on. "He'll get tired and turn back," I reckoned. I reckoned wrong.

I climbed briskly up the steep, winding trail, moving fast, working up a lather and putting my lung power to the test. All the while, the dog stayed with me. At times, he bolted ahead, putting about twenty yards between us before stopping and waiting for me to catch up. Then he'd let me pass and, trailing right behind, he'd press his snout into my calves as if telling me to *hele mai*, move faster.

Even when the pitch of the path steepened to hand-over-foot scrambling, the persistent canine pressed on. Reaching the first major knob in the ridge, an eroded hill with a nice view of Kāne'ohe Bay, I stopped and congratulated my now-initiated hiking companion by caressing his brown-and-black coat and stroking his teepee-like ears.

"You're going all the way, huh, brah?" I queried. His eyes, black like watermelon seeds, were trained on me as if he understood what I'd just asked.

We continued on for another fifteen minutes, pausing at "C-Rock," a rock face where a couple of generations of Castle High students have painted and repainted a huge "C" for the windward community to see.

The improved trail ended at C-Rock, and I retrieved a machete from my pack so I could continue hacking my way along the ridge toward Hawaiian Memorial Park. Because of encroaching vegetation, the going was much slower from then on, but the shep moved along patiently with me.

While I chopped along, he hung back a few yards, as if knowing an errant swing could hack off a paw. And when I paused to rest, he moved next to me, inviting a pat on the head. I always obliged. When I fetched my water bottle from my pack, he moved to my side, waiting for a sip. Using the palm of my left hand as a water dish, I obliged him then, too.

After each rest break, I continued my labor, chopping away at barriers of Christmas berry and guava. Every now and again the shep would dash off into the brush along the ridge, pouncing on some insect or rodent my meager human senses couldn't detect. He'd be gone for a few minutes. Then, without fail, he'd reappear.

Gradually, we worked our way to the highest *pu'u* on the ridge, a point, according to topo maps, with a fairly lofty elevation of 942 feet. Resting in a small clearing with a splendid southeast view of Mount Olomana and beyond to Makapu'u Point, we shared the last of our water. I congratulated my friend again, for his endurance, his patience, his companionship.

Although a faint trail continued along the ridge, I decided we'd done enough for the day and backtracked along the route we'd ascended. The trail cleared now, we moved easily and quickly on the downward journey.

Thirty minutes later, we neared the trailhead. Seeming to recognize the lay of the area, the shep jogged ahead of me more often. Always, though, he paused for me to catch up. Was he waiting for me to show him the way? Or was he checking if I was all right?

When I reached my car, the dog paused momentarily by my side for what was to be my final pat. While I fumbled with a pocket in my pack to get my keys, the dog trotted off to the hedge where I'd first seen him. When I looked up again, he'd disappeared. "Probably went home to get something to eat and drink," I thought.

That night, when I recounted my story to my younger brother, Alika, he asked if I knew about the *heiau* (Kawaʻewaʻe) in the area near the trail. "That was a spirit dog," he asserted. "He went along with you to make sure you were safe on your hike."

Chicken skin time.

Was my brother right? A hardcore skeptic, I was convinced the dog was real. He was there with me. I touched his silky coat, heard his breath, saw him dashing about, felt him lap water from my hand.

Or did I? Was he really a spirit, an *ʻaumakua* shielding me from harm?

Though I may never know for sure, it's clear I couldn't have had a better hiking partner than that exquisite, steadfast, and loyal animal——real or otherwise—accompanying me on that spring day along Kokokahi Ridge.

Born and raised on Oʻahu's windward side, Dayle Turner is a graduate of the Kamehameha Schools, University of Hawaiʻi (B.A.), and Northern Arizona University (M.A.). He teaches reading and writing courses at Leeward Community College and is a hike leader for the Hawaiian Trail and Mountain Club.

She moved from Texas to Hawai'i, got a job, found a condo. Life was good. She'd heard about the strange things that happen in Hawai'i, but never thought it would happen to her. One day, while home alone, she sensed a spirit in her condo. What unfolded became the haunting nightmare of . . .

A Malihini's *First Impressions*

I was new to the islands, as I had moved from Austin, Texas, four months earlier, in October 1996. I had rented a condo off H-1 around Kīnaʻu and Victoria. I wasn't aware of local ghost stories and didn't even know what "chicken skin" was! No matter what you call it, I experienced first-class, full-on haunting.

It started one day while I was still unemployed. I had been in the condo only a few days. I was sitting in my den, an enclosed *lānai*. In front of my desk was a window to the kitchen area, leftover from the days when the *lānai* was still an open area.

As I sat there, typing on my computer, I kept seeing something out of the corner of my eye. Sometimes, it was off to the left, and sometimes directly above, coming through the window. Each time I looked up, nothing was there.

Later, my partner, Beth, who had lived in the islands sixteen years, came home for lunch. "I don't think I'm alone here," I said, and told her what I'd seen, or thought I'd seen.

"Talk to it next time you see it," she said. "Tell it you don't mean any harm."

Next time it happened, I was alone and, taking Beth's advice, spoke to whoever, or whatever, it was: "Hello," I said. "I don't mean you any harm. I'm here peacefully." I was sincere when I said it, although I felt a bit creepy.

Whatever it was stopped after that (although I was told later that I never should have spoken to the person I saw at the corner of my eye). I figured either I was imagining the whole thing in the first place, or it was satisfied with my response to its presence.

Some nights later I was sleeping in my bedroom and had the first of many nightmares. The dream started with a "picking" at my toes. I awoke and thought it was our kitten playing with my feet. But then the picking stopped, and the bed began to shake—lightly at first. I still thought it was the kitten scratching. But the shaking got harder and harder. I got so scared I started screaming, then realized it was all a dream.

Beth woke up too, of course. I told her everything that happened in the dream. I had such a feeling of dread and evil. But I figured it was just another of the many bad dreams I'd had in my life. "Everybody has nightmares from time to time," I said.

As months progressed, nightmares continued. They got worse—stronger—and the scene was always my bedroom. The worst nightmares were the ones in which I felt like I couldn't breathe. In the dream I'd feel suddenly unable to catch my breath, eventually not able to breathe at all. I would wake up choking and gasping for air.

I had these nightmares about two or three nights a week, and before long, I was afraid to go to sleep at night. I started taking sleeping pills to try to make it through the night. I thought I should see a therapist. I had always been told that dreams are your subconscious trying to tell you something.

By then I was working, and I came dragging to work one morning after a night of little sleep. "What's up with you?" a colleague asked. "You look exhausted."

I told him about my dreams. He introduced me to a co-worker who said I was experiencing a classic haunting by a "sitting ghost " and told me how to remedy the situation.

That day I put ti plants in the four corners of my bedroom and sprinkled Hawaiian salt around the perimeter. This made all the difference! I finally got some sleep! As long as I kept the salt and the ti in place, I had no problem sleeping. Occasionally, I forgot, and the salt would get vacuumed up in the weekly cleaning. Far too often, the ghosts let me know this by harassing me in my sleep. The strange thing was that Beth never was harmed by the ghosts, only me! Until January of 1988, that is.

I had back surgery and had to sleep on her side of the bed, closer to the bathroom. That night, it was Beth who sat up gasping with something on her chest! This only happened to her once. She yelled at it to leave her alone. I tried this too but it never worked for me. Then new things started to happen.

It was as if every time we did something to stop them there were more of them and they were more angry. The ghosts seemed to leave the dream world and enter the physical. Things started falling off the walls and the bookshelves. Lights turned themselves on. The toilet would flush itself.

At that point I sought the help of a *kahuna*. She came over to the house and performed a blessing and exorcism. And it worked for some time. But about two months later I woke up to the sound of knocking coming from inside our closet. I woke up Beth, asked if she heard it, and she said she did. I asked if she would mind going and seeing what it was. She reluctantly said okay. Just as she stood up, the knocking stopped.

We were getting desperate for help. When a house we wanted came open for rent we decided to leave our condo with the great location and seek refuge in Kuli'ou'ou Valley. We moved in February 1998, but before we left, the haunting rose to a fever pitch. It was so bad that after we set up house at our new residence, Beth asked me not to come back to the condo, since obviously I was the primary target.

Even though she had escaped most of the turmoil, once I was gone, the ghosts bothered her just as badly, by turning her vacuum cleaner off and on. She told me later that she yelled out to them, "We're getting out as fast as we can! But you have to let me vacuum!" Finally, she finished cleaning up and closed the door to the condo for the last time. She had scrubbed and cleaned the refrigerator with ammonia, yet a few days later it was found totally trashed and roach-infested! There had been only a few roaches in our apartment the entire time we lived there. This not only shocked us but left us with the feeling our ghosts had given us a final warning: "Get out and stay out!"

We rarely tell this tale, as so many things could be considered just coincidence. But others recognize that what happened to us is just a part of living on these spiritually active islands. I tell this story now because I think it's important that people new to the islands not take these things lightly. Five years into my life here, I have a healthy respect for the spirits of Hawai'i *nei*, both good and bad!

Scottie Shelton was born in Fort Worth, Texas, in 1955, and raised in Dallas. She went to school there and later to college, where she studied music. Shelton moved to Austin in 1983 and worked as an electrician for a municipally owned power plant for fourteen years. She came to Hawai'i for the first time in 1996 to visit an old college friend who'd lived here since 1980. After seeing Hawai'i from a local's perspective, Shelton was completely captivated by the islands. She went home, sold all her worldly possessions, and moved to Honolulu six weeks later. At the time of the haunting she worked at Tokai University as Facility Manager. She is now employed by REHAB Hospital of the Pacific as the Plant Operations Manager, and lives in the quiet of Kuli'ou'ou Valley, where she sleeps peacefully every night.

Often they gathered in Ka'a'awa on Friday nights at Honey's house on Kamehameha Highway across from the beach to sip champagne, enjoy great meals, and share good times. Everything about those evenings seemed wonderful, except the long, dark ride home from the country. It all had something to do with . . .

Uncle Eddie

Uncle Eddie was different. He married a lady from England and they had no children. They lived in Kaʻaʻawa across Kamehameha Highway from the beach. Next door in the three-home compound his sister, Aunty Lani, had her country home. Honey, the other sister and my grandmother, had her country home next door to Aunty Lani's. We went to the country home frequently as I grew up. Then, after Grandpa died and the freeway went through their property in Kaimukī, Honey moved to Kaʻaʻawa. Sometimes I visited her for a few days, and my cousin Anna stayed there while attending Church College, now Brigham Young University-Hawaiʻi.

But back to Uncle Eddie. He was well known in Kaʻaʻawa. He was always meeting someone, conferring, bringing out water and ti leaves and sprinkling them. He worked for the city auditor's office and would take the big Windward Taxi to and from work at City Hall in downtown Honolulu. Somehow, he'd get the weekly serials, the ones usually seen in movie theaters, like "The Shadow Knows" and others, all in black and white. So on Friday nights, everyone, or so it seemed, gathered at his large patio to enjoy the latest serials, shown using his ancient projector and a large sheet hung from the rafters. Sometimes he'd watch and sometimes not, for he'd be praying and such in another part of the house, sort of like a *kahuna* or something.

When I stayed over, Anna and I would drink champagne. She loved it. And so did Honey. Sometimes, we'd tease Honey, saying that we didn't want to invite Aunty and Uncle because they'd drink too much and leave less for us. Honey would lecture and we would recant, saying that we were just teasing.

One night Uncle Eddie and Aunty Alice came over and all us were going strong. We ate dinner at Honey's large dinner table and continued to consume champagne. Then, out of the blue, Uncle Eddie said to me, "I see the ghost of George Fern above your head."

I immediately felt a strange feeling up and down my back.

Honey said, "Don't be silly, Eddie!"

Well, I had heard the name before. George Fern was one of my grandfather's relatives, and he and his wife were childless and had wanted to adopt my father. I am named after my father, for I am Ellwood L. Fern, Jr.

Why would George Fern's ghost visit me—or was it Uncle Eddie's imagination? I had never felt that before, an instant chill up and down my spine that did not go away. I stood up and said, "Goodbye!" I left in my Volkswagen bug and headed home, although I was supposed to stay over at Honey's.

My car stalled at the top of the hill entering Kualoa. It stalled again in Hakipuʻu. And again in Kahaluʻu. I pushed the car each time and it started. At Hygienic

Store, it stalled again. I turned and screamed, "Leave me alone!" I pushed, it started, I drove home to Kuliʻouʻou without another stall.

The next day I went to my regular service station and my car was thoroughly checked. Nothing was wrong, and it never stalled again in all the time I owned it.

I don't know how I escaped from George Fern's ghost. I never want to feel that chill or go through that again!

Storyteller extraordinaire Woody Fern grew up in Kaʻaʻawa on Oʻahu's windward side; he is the great-grandnephew of the first mayor of Honolulu, Joseph Fern. Woody lectures at Kapiʻolani and Windward community colleges, Lanakila Senior Citizen Center, the Hawaiʻi Maritime Museum, Kamehameha Schools, and Hawaiʻi Pacific University. He has trained docents at Washington Place and coached students in Stevenson Intermediate's annual speech competition. With Nyla Fujii-Babb of the Hawaiʻi State Public Library System, he developed an innovative program, "Nurturing Self-Esteem through Storytelling," that helps local students learn about their heritage and themselves.

Pueo *Tales*

A little gray bird with big yellow eyes, the Hawaiian owl, or *pueo*, barks like a dog and screams like a cat. Native Hawaiians traditionally consider the *pueo* a guardian spirit, as we discover in three stories, two new, the other old.

Pueo *Tales*

A *Pueo* Blessing

Paula and Wayne Sterling

Huli mai nānā i ka pulapula.
Turn, behold your offspring.
   – Prayer to family *'aumakua*

There were no cars on the highway as we left Kaua'i's Wilcox Hospital that May morning. At least we didn't notice any. We were oblivious to everything but our new infant. Born three days earlier, Rebecca Lilinoekeka-pahauomaunakea was going home, home to anxiously waiting siblings John, Malia, and Caroline. We were excited, too, yet enjoyed the intimacy of the moment, just Mom, Dad, and baby.

We decided to drive the "long way" home. I don't know why, we just did, maybe for the serenity, and by way of introducing our newborn daughter to the island. We turned left at the Coco Palms Hotel, went uphill past 'Ōpaeka'a Falls, and behind Nounou Mountain—the

Sleeping Giant. There, the winding road stretched out below us as wide swaths of green gently rose to meet the distant hills and cloud-covered peaks. It was so incredibly beautiful and peaceful, and our precious infant slept.

As we followed the winding road's descent toward Kapaʻa, a low-flying bird swept across the road just ahead of our car. It crossed back again, then kept pace on the driver's side for at least a hundred yards before the road curved away from its flight path. We could see it was a *pueo*. Wayne remarked how unusual it was to see one at that time of day. The road straightened out once again, and we saw an incredible sight up ahead. The *pueo* was perched on a fencepost along the roadside. As we passed, it took flight, our escort once more.

Again, it crossed our path once, twice, then doubled back, circling low just above the fence line, where it remained with us a few moments more before heading west toward the high mountains beyond.

It was a chicken skin moment. The *pueo* is one of Wayne's family *ʻaumākua*. Could we have been blessed with a visit? It surely felt so. It was difficult *not* to believe that the newest member of our family had received a special sign of welcome. Curious *pueo,* or *ʻaumakua*? Either way, we had witnessed something very special, and we definitely counted the *pueo*'s appearance as an added blessing that morning.

Paula Sterling is a graduate of Punahou Academy and Lake Forest College. As a young girl she lived in Indonesia and Japan, where her father was a foreign service officer with the U.S. Department of State. She has had a variety of careers, the most important raising her children and helping them find their gifts.

Wayne Sterling, also a graduate of Punahou Academy, has a degree in hotel management from the University of Hawai'i. He is currently general manager of the Outrigger Waikiki on the Beach. His hotel career has enabled the family to live in Tahiti and American Samoa, enriching their lives and expanding their interest in the cultures of Polynesia.

A *PUEO* SAVED MY LIFE

KATHY TRETSVEN

A *pueo* saved my life; honest, it's true. It happened about twenty years ago on Kaua'i, but I'll never forget it. I was coming home from Waimea. In those days I stayed at Kōke'e, up on the mountain at the end of the long winding road. I had too much to drink, way too much at a party in Waimea.

I wasn't even sure how to get back. I just set off driving up the mountain. All of a sudden this huge thing hit the car, hit the windshield.

Whoa! What was that? I pulled over to the side of the road and stopped. It was a beautiful *pueo*. It struck the windshield and then flew away. It wasn't hurt; it just flew away.

It sure sobered me up. My heart was pounding. With all of the adrenaline in me I felt fine, I felt much better, suddenly sober, and I drove all the way home without a problem. I don't drink anymore, not like those days, anyway, and when I see a *pueo* I remember that night and say a little prayer of thanks.

Kathy Tretsven, a Chaminade University graduate who has lived on Oʻahu for thirty years, works as an accountant and has four children.

A HISTORIC ENCOUNTER

RICK CARROLL

Valdemar Knudsen, a Norwegian adventurer who struck it rich in the 1849 California gold rush, landed in Hawaiʻi six years later, and really struck it rich. He learned to speak Hawaiian, leased one hundred square miles of western Kauaʻi from King Kamehameha IV, raised cattle, and became known as Aliʻi o Kauaʻi, the Lord of Kauaʻi.

Knudsen "discovered" the Hawaiian stilt, which the Smithsonian Institute named after him: *Himantopus mexicanus knudseni*. He also discovered the spiritual power of the *pueo*.

While out riding one day, Knudsen encountered forty fluffy owls, which he knew to be a sign. He reined in his horse and, for a moment, stood all alone amid the owls.

Most of the owls soon disappeared, but three flew around his head, brushed his hat, then disappeared. The owls had revealed themselves to be his *ʻaumakua*, or guardian spirit.

They appeared again another day to keep him from harm. He was riding fast on a west Kauaʻi cliff trail when an owl flew into his horse's face. His steed shied and leaped sideways off the trail. Knudsen dismounted to find just ahead in his path two large, ferocious wild boars.

His *'aumakua*, the owl, saved him from what likely would have been a deadly encounter.

Author and photo-journalist Rick Carroll is the collector of the six books of stories in the *Hawai'i's Best Spooky Tales* series. His latest book, *Huahine: Island of the Lost Canoe*, is a true-life archaeological mystery set in the Society Islands.

Sacred Ground

Kalalau is a valley, a waterfall and a beach. It is best known for a footpath, a thin zigzag trail across Kauaʻi's sheer Nā Pali coast. One misstep and it's *limu* time. Nimble men with guns once hunted goats on the trail; sometimes they found more than wild game out there . . .

Hunting Kalalau

Years ago it was said that during certain summer months at the Kalalau Valley lookout on the island of Kaua'i, you could hear horses running down on the Kalalau Trail. They were said to be ghosts of long-ago horses that once galloped the trails with Hawaiian warriors seeking victory over enemies. One could experience this eerie phenomenon in the natural silence when the wind was just so. We were told this sacred ground should be respected, and anyone who ventured here should heed warnings.

During the depression in the early fifties, there was no work, no income, and no food for the stevedores and plantation workers and their families who lived in the plantation camp. In order for us to survive, the men would hunt for any fresh game they could find. I remember my dad and the rest of the men bringing home deer, wild pigs, goats, and fish for the wives to cook in the camp soup kitchen. What was so extraordinary was that our camp consisted of so many different cultures, yet we all worked side by side and helped one another survive during this depression.

On one particular day while my dad and his friends

were getting ready for another hunt, he told them they were going to Kalalau Valley to hunt the Kalalau Trail. He warned them to kill only what they needed and what they could carry home, since some hunters who left fresh kills behind had unusual things happen to them.

After they had gathered their fresh kill of goat and wild pigs, my dad told the others to leave the bones and skin behind and to take only what they needed. If not, they would find the pack too heavy to carry. He told them to gather bamboo stalks and sharpen them at the ends and poke them into the bags, one to the left, one to the middle, and one to the right of the bag, making sure the pointed ends stuck out.

As my dad was preparing the bamboo for his pack, a hunter asked my dad the reason for this. My dad said, "Just do as I tell you and you will find that we will have no problems going down this mountain."

The other fellow said he didn't believe in that and laughed about it.

My dad picked up his pack, threw it across his back and headed down the trail. While the others followed, this guy yelled out to my dad: "Eh, something stay on my back pack. I no can carry dis buggah, too heavy. Feel like somebody stay holding me back."

My dad turned around and said: "I told you to do what I said and you no like listen, now you gotta leave your pack behind."

My dad had no fear of the supernatural. He experienced so many unbelievable things, yet accepted them with the highest respect for ancient Hawaiians. He always believed there was a reason for everything and that we must teach our children to respect the island and its mysteries.

We survived because he tramped all over this island gathering food for us. If he came home successful, with fresh food, it was a good omen. Once when he and some others went fishing on high seas behind Polihale, their boat capsized and they lost all their catch. Coming home empty-handed, he said, "I guess that was meant to be, guess the fish had to stay back." He never got upset about it but accepted it with honor. Of course, we didn't have any fresh food that week except for leftovers caught the week before.

When I think back and realize how fortunate we were to always have food on the table, I thank God I had such a wonderful, strong, and resourceful father. He respected sacred ground and in return was blessed as being one of the best fishermen and hunters known on Kaua'i during his time. God rest his soul, my dad.

Joyce Guzman was born on Kaua'i and graduated from Waimea High School. She now lives in Dana Point, California. Her stories "The Grandma Who Talked to Ghosts," "A Moonlit Night at Anahola," "Grandma's Finally at Rest," and "Sacred Fishing Grounds" appeared in *Hawai'i's Best Spooky Tales 4.*

When a young Honolulu
boy explored an old
Hawaiian burial cave in the
sixties and removed certain
small objects, he had
no idea that his life
would be haunted unless
he returned . . .

The Purloined Beads

As a scientist, I like to consider myself strictly objective when it comes to observing and describing events. My background in neuroscience and statistics and my research demand that I be methodical and precise in my collection of data and interpretations of my observations. Perhaps the most unlikely word that friends and acquaintances would use to describe me would be "superstitious."

Yet ever since middle school I have had a continuous run of misfortune. You could ask my parents, Claire and Jerry. Or my best friend, Gordon. He always used to say that bad things happened to him. After he got married and we stopped spending much time together, his luck improved but mine didn't. Gordon now claims jokingly that all along I was the bad influence.

I think my misfortune can be traced to the early sixties, in Hawai'i, where my dad was a music professor at the University of Hawai'i. And I think things may have changed for the worse that day we found a cave up in the Ko'olau Mountains.

My brother, David, and I, along with two pals, used to hike into the mountains high above Ali'ikoa Street on

Oʻahu, where I grew up. Once, we hiked four or five hours along ridges and through what seemed like miles of thick underbrush until we came upon a lava tube cave. The cave had a very wide opening that rapidly narrowed at the back, leading to a low opening (maybe a foot high) exposing pitch-black nothingness beyond. We dared each other to crawl on our bellies under the opening and into the blackness, but we all chickened out.

The next trip we wisely brought flashlights and sack lunches. On this occasion, and perhaps several others, we actually did slide on our bellies under the low shelf at the back of the cave and enter a chamber that appeared to be a burial ground or other sacred site. We found pieces of bones and a number of pieces of what appeared to be some sort of holding vessel, and beads scattered around in dirt on the floor. We were in awe then and each time we visited this cave. I recall that we always whispered.

On one of our visits to this cave, I took two or three small, colorful beads that I found on the floor of the cave and, unobserved by my pals, stuck them in my pocket. I don't know why; it was just an impulsive kid-thing to do.

A few hours after we arrived at the cave, after we finished our sack lunches, the cave grew really dark, darker than usual. One of us walked to the mouth of the cave and discovered that a big storm appeared to be brewing. We decided to begin our two-to-three–hour hike back home, and just as we were about to leave the cave, a very thin figure suddenly appeared inside the mouth of the cave.

Strangely, we had not heard any sound warning of his

presence in the cave. As he approached us, we grew very quiet and scared. Who was this man? How did he get way up here? How could he possibly have climbed the mountain at his age?

We were speechless and frozen in our tracks. We were so scared as the man approached that maybe we only imagined the details about him. He seemed quite old—maybe too old—to boys of ten to thirteen years of age. In fact, from our perspective, he seemed ancient. He had a long grayish white beard and a cane or walking stick. We could not understand the harsh language he spoke. However, I recall that we did hear the word *kapu* a few times, mixed in with the man's apparently angry dialogue.

It did not take long for one of us, I think Cutty, to yell, "Run!" And run we did! I think we ran the entire way back down the mountain.

Many days later, or it might have been weeks, we made subsequent trips to the cave area. We never saw the old man again. But we scouted the area for possible paths, or other ways that he could have made it to the cave. I remember that behind the cave was a steep cliff, and the only other way up or down was the way we had come. We were convinced that this man could not possibly have climbed to the cave.

Years went by and I forgot all about the beads from the cave, which I put in a glass vial with other rocks and shells and things I found in other places. It all became part of an ongoing collection, which I kept in a box in my closet.

I moved from Hawai'i with my parents and brother in the late 1960s. As I grew up on the mainland, strange things kept happening to me.

In 1973, I attended Rutgers University as a first-year college student. When I returned from a weekend visit to my parents' home, my roommate Juan, from Puerto Rico, sat me down and began to describe an experience he had on the Friday evening that he was alone in the dorm room.

He was visibly shaken and white in the face as he recounted the experience. He told me he was in bed trying to go to sleep when the door to the room opened quietly.

He opened his eyes, thinking it was either me or our third roommate (who also had left for the weekend). He saw two large figures enter the room and open the sliding doors to my closet. He claimed they appeared to be searching for something for nearly ten minutes. They said nothing and made absolutely no noise in the closet. They then left as quietly as they had entered the room.

Juan said the intruders were scantily clad in shorts or loincloths. I do not recall whether I had told him about the beads before or after he related this experience to me.

I do not remember if I actually took those beads with me when I went to Puerto Rico in 1982 as a Ph.D. student in marine science, but strange things kept happening to me there.

Twice while I was conducting underwater research off the coast of La Paguera, Puerto Rico, I ran out of air while SCUBA diving. I was a well-trained and certified diver with many hours of underwater experience. I always checked and double-checked all my equipment and procedures before descending. On both occasions, my air supply ran out as I approached the depth of eighty feet. The dive master at University of Puerto Rico determined that the air tanks had malfunctioned. He told me this had never happened before even once, let alone twice!

One year later, in the El Junque rain forest in Puerto Rico, where I had stopped for lunch, my car was stolen with all of my research data.

Almost everywhere I have ever rented, there has been a flood. In Nutley, New Jersey, in 1984, the pipe broke in the ceiling of my rented house, ruining all my clothes and my bed. In 1993, in Montclair, New Jersey, all the toilets in the apartment building in which I lived flooded out through my toilet. My entire apartment was flooded in sewage water. And then again in the same apartment, in 1997, the tenant living above me forgot to turn off his sink faucet, and again my entire apartment was flooded.

In 1986, I visited Hawai'i Volcanoes National Park on the Big Island. I gathered such items as Pele's hair, interesting small pieces of lava, green and black sand, and burned wood taken from the latest eruption. I took these items back to the East Coast with me, planning to donate them to the American Museum of Natural History in New York, where I was conducting my Ph.D. research.

I had numerous discussions about these items with a native Hawaiian friend before boarding my flight home. She begged me to leave them on the Big Island, where she felt the gods wanted them to be and where they belong.

However, I did not follow her advice and took them with me in my luggage for the flight home. On that flight, I was daydreaming about the exciting time I had had and the memorabilia I was taking back. As the flight attendants began to serve dinner, I thought of my friend and her warnings about the consequences of taking those items off the Big Island. Then I had a crazy thought: *If there was any truth to what my friend said about taking those things from the volcano area and the ancient spirits and gods becoming angry, show me a sign.*

Within a few seconds, the plane hit an air pocket and abruptly dropped a few thousand feet. Thank God nobody was hurt. When the screaming passengers quieted and the food was being cleaned off the ceiling of the cabin, I vowed to return the items I took the minute I touched ground in Newark. And that is just what I did.

It sounds odd now, but I never thought of the beads and the rocks in the same context. When I returned to Hawai'i in August 1999, with my cat, Bouchette, I brought the beads with me. They are still packed in a box marked "rocks" in the little glass vial that I first put them into back in the early sixties. I had planned to return the beads to the cave, but strange things started happening before I could find them and return them.

First, my cat, an otherwise perfectly healthy Himalayan, was diagnosed with a very bad heart murmur, indicative of heart disease. Then her kidneys failed. Also, she has had to be on continuous antibiotics due to a chronic urinary tract inflammation. As a result of all these ailments, she lost about a third of her weight.

Then my love life failed, and I lost my job at the university, and the entire house that I rented flooded with sewage water that came up on its own simultaneously from both toilet and bath.

I've started my own consulting firm—that's one positive—but I am still having misfortune, and I haven't found those beads. I am looking for them even now.

At last, I found the beads.

I opened the container and looked at what appeared to be three small, rather typical-looking, perfectly round stringing beads. The beads were all the same size, but one was red, one was yellow, and one was green.

My girlfriend was with me, and we both agreed that they looked like ordinary manufactured beads sold for stringing. I was rather disappointed, because I recalled them to be of different sizes, irregular in shape, and of more than one color.

I attributed the discrepancies between what I remembered and what I saw to the many years that had passed. We all know that time has a way of altering memories.

I made plans to return the beads with the help of a *kahuna* friend of my girlfriend who has much experience in Hawaiian ancestral history and in handling the return of sacred artifacts.

Before returning the beads, I took one last look. What I observed made the hair on the back of my neck stand up. There were now four beads, not three! One bead, the red one, was three times larger than the others. This bead was irregularly shaped and had white circles painted around the holes at both ends! The smaller red bead now also had white circles around its holes!

I called my girlfriend, who looked at the beads and appeared shaken at what she now saw.

The *kahuna* met me early the next morning, and we wrapped in ti leaves offerings such as *poi* and dried shrimp along with the beads in their container. He helped me find an appropriate place on the same mountain where I found the beads. Prayers were said to clear our path as we walked and again at the place the wrapped beads and offerings were left.

The *kahuna* asked that I not mention his name or details about the return of the beads. However, I would like to mention that he explained to me that there is nothing evil in what was happening to me since I took those beads from a burial ground. He told me that the beads were probably left to honor the dead and that they probably were, or were related to, something the dead person loved. He said that this was all about *aloha*, including why the beads were placed in the cave in the first place and the experiences I had over the years.

Apparently, it was all about doing the correct thing by returning the beads to their proper place to the best of my ability. He made me realize that perhaps one of the most important consequences of telling my story would be my helping to dispel the notion that evil is a part of experiences related to Hawaiian burial grounds.

I do not know if my persistent pattern of misfortune

will change because I have returned the beads. But I do believe I have taken the appropriate action by attempting to return the beads to the proper owner.

Robert E. Landsman, who spent his boyhood on Oʻahu, is a research scientist and a consultant specializing in science education and statistics. A Rutgers University graduate, Landsman earned his masters degree in bioethics, experimental psychology, and biopsychology, and a Ph.D. in biopsychology/neuroscience from The Graduate School and University Center of the City University of New York. He has published numerous papers in the fields of neuroscience. His most notable research findings focus on why feral animals brought into captivity fail to reproduce. He now heads his own Hawaiʻi firm, ANOVA Science Education Consulting, at anovaone@aol.com.

Oh, look, it's a
parade! And it's coming
down your street.
A delighted little Maui girl
watches the parade go by her
house. She runs inside to get
her mother, and returns
only to discover something
very spooky about . . .

The Procession

Hawai'i is one of the most spiritual places in the world. We have the spirits of ancient Hawai'i—kings and other royalty, *menehune*, night marchers—as well as ghosts who are angry or lonely or just want to have fun.

Most encounters people have with ghosts in Hawai'i occur in a place where something was established or where something important happened—a *heiau*, a burial site, or even an old Hawaiian fishing village—or where something unjust happened to an innocent person.

But when you have an encounter with a bunch of ghosts like I did, you try to understand the reasons you saw them and nobody else did. Maybe you're gifted or were chosen for some reason. You remember what happened and you just try to piece together the puzzle to find out the truth.

One day when I was about six years old, I was sitting out in front of my house waiting for my mom to get off the phone so we could go to the beach. I was relaxing under a little palm tree that I had just helped plant. All of a sudden I heard the rhythmic beating of drums down my street. I was thinking, "Wow! There is a parade on my street! Oh, cool!"

I kept on watching and then started clapping. The

marchers turned their heads and smiled. I smiled back. They were dressed in traditional Hawaiian clothes. Not a single one was wearing clothes from the missionary times. A few had red and yellow capes. I had never seen a parade like that before.

I ran into the house to get my mom, who was still on the phone. When I ran in I cut myself on the screen door. I kept bugging my mom until she got off the phone and told her to come outside with me to watch the parade. She looked at me, surprised, and let me drag her outside.

When we got to the exact place I had been watching from, they were gone. I couldn't understand how a long line of people could be gone in five minutes. It didn't make sense. I looked up and down the street for them, but I didn't see any trace of them. They had really disappeared!

Later that day, I asked a couple of our neighbors, who were doing yard work when the procession went by, if they had seen or heard anything that day. They said no.

My mom said she believed me about the parade. But since I was so young, I didn't think she really believed I saw anything. But I knew what I saw. The people looked real. They weren't floating or transparent. I know that it wasn't a dream, because I still have the scar from running into the side of the screen door.

A couple of summers ago, I was in Honolulu and I wanted to visit 'Iolani Palace. As soon as I walked through the front gates, I got this strong energy all around me. I couldn't tell what it was. But as soon as I stepped into the foyer of the house, I got a flash of the procession, the parade on my street from years ago. It was weird. As I was walking into the palace, I saw an image of one of the young ladies from the procession. It was as if history was trying to tell me something.

We toured the house, and nothing else happened until I entered the throne room, where I started hearing ballroom music. It was just as loud as the drums I had heard in the procession. I looked around to see if anyone else was hearing it too, but nobody mentioned anything. There were no speakers anywhere.

Then, this last Halloween, when I was trick-or-treating in my neighborhood with my auntie and my little cousin, I told my auntie about the procession. She said it made sense, because while some people were building their house earlier in the year, the contractors found bones. They were building a house on an ancient burial ground. That stopped the building for a couple of months.

All of the music, flashes, and everything else finally made sense. The procession could have taken place because someone important was visiting someone else at the burial ground. They might not have buried royalty down by the beach, but it could've been a procession for something else. Who knows, maybe our whole neighborhood is built on top of an old fishing village.

It made me more aware of the spirits around me and also made me glad to know I'm not insane. I leave everything where it is supposed to stay. I don't take lava rocks home. I don't remove anything from its natural habitat. I respect nature.

Noelle Barbosa is a student at Lahainaluna High School on Maui, class of 2004. She likes to write and to visit historical landmarks.

If you've never heard a
wild pig squeal in the forests
of Hawai'i, let me tell you,
it's a blood-curdling
scream that makes the hair
on the back of your neck
stand straight up.
Those who hunt wild pigs in
Hawai'i know what happens
out there in the woods.
Some dare to share the
spooky secret in this real-life
adventure story about . . .

Pig Hunters on Sacred Grounds

There is beauty in the land of Hawai'i that attracts all groups of people. Some areas are so full of history that Hawaiians say they are sacred, or *kapu*, which means "do not touch." Such places—old Hawaiian war, burial, and sacrificial sites—are little known to most people today, including some local, island-born feral pig hunters.

Most feral pig hunters will agree that they must watch where they step, especially if they lack knowledge of the history of the land. Sometimes, hunters experience supernatural activity that causes physical ailments and psychological trauma that defy any logical explanation. Skeptics may doubt such things happen, but I know better, because my husband and son and their pals are feral pig hunters and they have encountered things they can't explain.

On the island of Lāna'i one hunter I know decided to hunt, not knowing he had entered a Hawaiian burial site. Soon after the hunt, he became so ill he could not walk straight. This man was taken to a hospital in Honolulu. The doctors could not pinpoint the cause of his illness, so the family finally called a *kahuna*, or Hawaiian doctor. The *kahuna* performed a ritual that removed the curse.

After this curse was removed, the hunter's health improved immediately.

Parking a vehicle on familiar or unfamiliar sacred ground may invite another type of supernatural occurrence. This supernatural event involves physical suppression. I know because it happened to my husband, Al.

On a Friday night almost twenty years ago, he and three other men planned an overnight hunt in Waikāne Valley on the island of Oʻahu. They would sleep in Al's 1969 International pick-up truck and a trailer used for transporting the dogs.

Steven Napanoa, Jack (Steven's friend), Martin "Guesso" Rivera, and Al Kalua, Jr., left about ten o'clock at night from Al's Waokanaka home in Nuʻuanu. They made a quick stop at the 7-Eleven store in Nuʻuanu for gas and to stock up on food for the hunt.

This hunt would take them into a two-mile underground water tunnel into the back of Kahana Valley, and they would hunt back up over the saddleback into Waikāne Valley to the truck. Upon reaching Waikāne Valley, they entered through the security gate. The key to open the gate was right where uncle Ray Kamaka said it would be. They noticed it was a beautiful clear night as they continued on the four-and-one-half miles of winding dirt road that leads to the back of Waikāne Valley.

Reaching their destination, these four hunters decided to park next to the large jaboong tree. Everything was quiet and normal, and at one o'clock in the morning they proceeded to pitch a tent over the rear of the truck in case of morning showers. The plan was to rest till five o'clock before starting the hunt.

After they settled down they were ready to sleep. All was quiet except for the occasional growling of a few dogs in the trailer. Steven, being the tallest, slept in the front of the truck. Guesso, Jack, and Al stretched out in the back of the pick-up. Since Jack was the smallest and youngest, he slept between Guesso and Al. By one-thirty they were in a deep sleep.

Somewhere between three and three-thirty, Guesso and Al were suddenly awakened by the violent shaking of the truck and by the screams of young Jack. Lying on his back with a look of confusion in his eyes, one leg in the air and his arms desperately seeking someone or something to grab on to, Jack was strangely being quickly pulled out the back of the truck. As quickly as he was pulled out, he was back in the truck again. Al got up to look around to see if anyone was playing a joke on them. The dogs in the trailer were mysteriously growling, but no one was around.

Gusso and Al were in the back of the truck staring at each other and asking Jack, "What happened?"

He replied, "I don't know, somebody pulled me out of the truck."

Right then a huge dark shadow loomed over the back of the truck. It was Steven. His six-foot-two-inch, two-hundred-pound frame had a startling effect in the dark. He asked, "What is going on?" He had slept through the whole ordeal. The others tried to explain what had just happened to Jack.

Needless to say, no one got much sleep the rest of the early morning. But it did help them get an early start on the hunt.

Seeing Jack sliding out of the truck on his back with his arms flailing helplessly has been forever embedded in Al's mind since that beautiful starry night in Waikāne Valley in 1983. Although medical explanations are available, this true event cannot be explained by the scientific community.

That experience pales in comparison with the scare the hunters got on Maui the summer of 1985. Al remembers that summer quite well, since his wife was pregnant with his daughter, who was born in the middle of August.

Behilio Martinez, Louis Junior Perez, and Al went to Maui on a hunting trip. They had been planning this trip for over one month. They slept over at Roland Kihano's house (Behilio's nephew) and at four o'clock in the morning started their journey to Keʻanae Valley for the hunt. This valley is known for its abundance of beautiful waterfalls and lush scenery.

Upon reaching the end of the road, Al noticed a few Chinese headstones. He thought it was quite odd that they were so near the side of this desolate rocky trail to the back of the valley.

On the second day they went to the deep right side of the valley. This put the hunters high above the state botanical park. They encountered numerous diggings of feral pigs in the area.

At this time, the men noticed that not a dog was among them. They stood there waiting quietly, assuming the dogs would soon bark and the hunt would be on.

Then it came, about one-half mile ahead. The steady barking of the trackers and the squealing of a pig assured them that the dogs had secured their prey.

After fifteen to twenty minutes of continuous running, the hunters reached a large, dry streambed. Al noticed that some of the dogs were at the streambed and couldn't scale the steep embankment of the stream. They helped the dogs climb the embankment and reached the area of the commotion only to find nothing. The hunters were a little puzzled as they came back across the stream with all six dogs. They continued hunting and in a few short minutes later, there it was again.

The dogs took off again and started back down the river. This time the hunters heard dogs fighting with the pig. When the hunters got to the area, all the dogs came running back to them. The dogs looked more bewildered than the hunters. Hunting dogs were moving in every direction.

At this point the guys began asking each other what was going on. Behilio, who has been hunting well over forty years, said, "Something does not feel right; something is wrong." But being the hunters that they were, they refused defeat and continued the hunt.

Fifteen minutes down the trail it started again. Behilio said, "Wait! It does not sound right."

Al glanced back and told Behilio, "It sounds like they have him this time."

Against Behilio's better judgment, Al bolted toward the commotion. When he got there, again there was nothing to be seen.

Then he heard and saw it, not more than twenty feet from him, the grunting of the pig and the shaking of the bushes. Al seemed to be in the middle of this commotion.

He backed up and chambered a round in his 30-30 Winchester. The grunting and squealing of the pig stopped, but the tender leaves of the *'awapuhi* continued to shake. Al stood in bewilderment: one dog came out and glanced up at him as he ran past, while all the ginger bushes and guava trees around Al kept shaking with not as much as a mild breeze in the air.

Then as quickly as it started, it stopped. Al met up with Behilio and Junior. He told them something was wrong here and that they should leave right now! After forty-five minutes of a seventy- or eighty-degree–angle climb, they reached the top of the mountain and proceeded toward the truck, less than a hundred feet away.

The hunters rested on top of the mountain and decided to continue exploring. At four-thirty in the evening they gathered up all the dogs and headed back toward Wailuku to Roland's mother's house for dinner. Not much was said on the way back. Everyone still looked bewildered. Upon reaching Roland's mother's house, Roland's uncle, Paul Milo, met the hunters and asked, "How was the hunt and where did you go?"

As Al exited the truck, he told Paul that they just had a very unusual experience on the right side of Ke'anae Valley.

Before Al could tell what happened, Paul said he would never hunt there again. He proceeded to tell the hunters what happened to him eighteen years before while hunting.

His story took them step-by-step through a hunt just like the one the hunters had come from that day. At this point the hunters looked at each other with disbelief. No one said a word; enough had been said.

There will always be stories of supernatural activities that follow the beauty of the land on the islands of Hawai'i. Where this beauty takes you, whether you are a believer or a skeptic, you should always obtain knowledge of where you are to avoid supernatural activities.

Leona Kalua is a wife and a mother of three. She works full time at a retail store on the Big Island of Hawai'i, and is also a full-time student working toward a Liberal Arts degree. Her husband, Al Kalua, has hunted wild boar from O'ahu to the Big Island for twenty-two years. Al also lived three years on the East Coast, hunting everything from turtledoves to alligators from North Carolina to the swamps of Georgia. He works on the Big Island and coaches high school baseball.

A little boy left on a Maui beach late at night is all alone—except for . . .

Just Them, Passing Through

When I was a little kid many years ago on the island of Maui, where I grew up, I used to go fishing with my uncle and my dad, a lot. I was about eight or nine. It was quite a journey at that time, always at night.

My dad and uncle fished at one point on Honolua Bay and I would wait for them at Oneloa Bay. That's beyond Kapalua on the north shore of Maui on the road to Kahakuloa. Dad would leave me on the beach, make a little fire. My uncle would tell me, "Be still, stay there. Don't walk around. Sit down with your legs crossed."

I used to kind of wonder why.

Then one night we went fishing and Uncle left me at Oneloa Bay. He told me to sit still, no move, cross legs. So I sat there with my legs crossed, by myself, crying my heart out, wondering when they were coming back to get me.

Then I felt sand falling on my legs and I looked on both sides of where I was sitting on the beach and all I saw were huge footprints just appearing like a whole tribe came walking by. You know how sand kicks up when you walk? Well, it was kicking up behind the footprints and the sand was falling on me.

But I didn't see anything else. There was nothing except huge footprints appearing and sand kicking up and landing on my feet. I didn't dare to move. I just sat still, my legs crossed, and the sand kept falling.

When Uncle came back I told him, and he said, "Oh, yeah, it's just them going down to the ocean. They're going back home."

"Who?" I asked.

"Oh, just them," Uncle said. "It's just them, passing through."

"But I no see 'um, just footprints and sand kicking up."

Uncle just smiled at me and said: "When you're older you'll know."

When I got older I found out that over there, that's where they found the *heiau* at Oneloa. My cousin, Anthony Kekona, was the one who took care of it. He was like the guardian. I found out who was passing through, but, funny thing, you know even now, all grown up, with a son, I live on Oʻahu now, and I never go back there. No way.

Keoni Farias, born on Oʻahu, the son of a one-hundred–percent Hawaiian, grew up on Maui, where many of his family members still reside; he graduated from Kalani High School and now lives on Oʻahu, where he works for the city refuse department.

Old Kaka'ako

When he was a little boy
on O'ahu, Kaka'ako was
full of fun—not the boring
jumble of shops and
high-rises it is now.
There were mysterious little
white dogs, the remains of a
leper colony, a mortuary to
play hide-and-seek in,
and neighbors who liked
quiet Sunday mornings.
In his spooky memoir Al
Tolentino takes us back to his
days in . . .

Old Kakaʻako

ONE SPOOKY SUNDAY MORNING

When I was five-and-a-half I was so happy one Sunday before Christmas because my mother bought me two cap pistols, a Hopalong Cassidy hat, and cowboy boots. I was so happy I was out early in the morning, loaded up my cap pistols and went pop-pop-popping all around outside for about half an hour until the neighbors said, "Will you shut up!"

So I didn't do anything for a while and all of a sudden I heard humming—hmmmmmm—and kaboom! Whoa, what is it? I looked up in the sky, and planes were coming all angles, headed straight for Pearl Harbor; planes came so low I could see a torpedo right under the wing—a bomber, I guess.

I could see three pilots right inside and they were looking down to the left. I guess they were looking at me, or looking at who was that little Hopalong Cassidy down there. I shot at them but it came out blank.

I knew they were heading for Pearl Harbor. You could see all that billowing black smoke over there—baboom! baboom!

No high-rises, just Aloha Tower. You could see everything, planes coming in from Kāne'ohe, Diamond Head,
and the Ko'olau Mountains, right into Pearl Harbor.

All the neighbors came out—I guess they thought I
was shooting my pistols again, except the noise got too
loud—and they said, "Whoooooa, we are being
attacked!"

I wanted to see what was really going on. I climbed
the fence to see because the Zeros were coming down,
and they were shooting, strafing the three-story wooden
building, and you could see all the splinters going up.

My brother came out of the house and saw me standing on the fence, and the planes coming so low. He ran
and knocked me right off the fence just so the shots
would miss me. That was a spooky Sunday morning, I'll
tell you that much.

THE WHITE DOG OF KAKA'AKO

I grew up in Kaka'ako, next to the Royal Brewery,
not far from where the fire station is now, only when I
was a boy the fire station was a cemetery. I wonder if the
firemen know that.

Anyway, next to the brewery was a building everyone
called 553; that's one of the places where I lived with my
family when I was a little kid. It was a three-story wood-
en building, with steps to the left and steps to the right.

One evening, my brothers and I, we're walking home
from the movie theater, called Kewalo Theater. On our
way home there weren't too many houses, just a lot of
wooden buildings. I remember American Sanitary

Laundry on the right side, and as we came close to 553, that block had three large mango trees, common mango trees.

So, close to midnight, as we approached our home, my brother—he was ten years older than me—saw this little white dog sitting by one of the mango trees and he called the dog just normally, whistled at the dog, like that. And every time he whistled at the dog, the dog looked at him and he waggled his tail, and started to grow bigger.

I mean bigger—like he grew a foot bigger every time my brother whistled. My brother didn't believe it. He tried it again, and we all watched it. He called, the dog just grew. None of us believed what we saw. We were so scared we just stood there, staring, like, What is that?

When we finally ran away from the dog he must have grown maybe about six feet. He was so huge we were afraid afterward that we were whistling to a devil.

My brother said, "Go!" and we did; we ran in the house, and like all spooked kids, when we got scared we either went under the bed and hid ourselves or jumped in bed and covered our heads so we didn't see anything. That's just the way it happened.

So when we all got in the house I could hear someone pounding on the door. My brother got a board and nailed it across the door so nothing could get in the house and we were safe.

Next morning, we came outside and we saw a machete all full of blood. I don't know who did it. Maybe my brother went outside again. I don't know. All I know is no more whistling, no more growing white dog.

My brother never told us one way or the other. And we never asked. We never even talked about what we saw for the longest time.

I don't know why the dog kept growing but I think this was what Hawaiians call *mana*.

DEAD MAN COMING ALIVE

When I was about nine or eleven there was a leper colony on O'ahu, out on Sand Island; that's where it was before it moved to Moloka'i, and they still had a couple of patients there yet, three or four sitting around under trees, waiting to pass away, I guess, or go to Kalaupapa.

The animals were still there, geese and chickens, and supplies, things like irons and clothing, waiting to be moved out to Moloka'i. The buildings with all the coffins were still there. That was all that was left of the colony.

We used to go there and play hide-and-seek. You know: you hide and I find you. We had secret places; we used to climb up on the trees, and stay on the branch when they came looking for us.

My favorite spot was hiding in one of the coffins. In that building they had coffins and all these appliances and everything. So I lay in one of the coffins, put the head latch down. My brother Jose looked all over the place and couldn't find me anywhere. I knew he was going to come in there, because I heard somebody say, "I saw him go in that building there."

So, when he came into the building I could hear him moving around, looking around behind cabinets and everything, and finally he said, "I wonder . . . ?"

When he opened that top latch, I lay still and he went, "Oooops," and I opened my eyes and he jumped ten feet high. He thought I was a dead man coming alive. And that was so much fun.

We were playing like that for about a week until finally the caretaker said, "No more playing over here. Everything's gonna be graded down." They knocked it all down, everything moved to Moloka'i, and no more hide-and-seek.

THE HEADLESS CORNER OF SAND ISLAND

As kids, sometimes we'd go to Sand Island to swim. We would go late at night to the lagoon where they fix the fishing boats. We would swim sometimes from ten or eleven o'clock to midnight.

When we came back from swimming around midnight—there was a cut trail along the fence—we used to hear a horse's hooves. Clop, clop, clop—a horse's hooves coming down.

And we looked around and we didn't believe what we saw. We all ran so fast. Even my brother. (My brother was never afraid of anything. He was the last one to run all the time.)

We saw this black shiny horse coming, and what's sitting on there? A woman. She had a veil over her face. And there was a guy with her, like a servant, just pulling the horse, walking with her, around that bend right there where they used to keep the animals at the leper colony, and the guy was more or less headless.

And when we saw that we just ran; we saw that for about a week, and then it completely disappeared.

We used to call that "the headless corner," because that's where we used to hear the horse's footsteps and see the headless man.

A BIG STRANGER ON THE TOUR BUS

Many years after our Sand Island days, I drove a tour bus. It started out as Rainbow Coach and then Trans-Hawaiian, and the bus yard was close to the Bitumulls area. That's what they called it. Bitumulls.

We had a yard there where we parked our buses, and the wash crew, anytime after midnight when they'd be washing the buses, could hear the dogs barking, but no dogs. If you went in the back you could hear dogs, but there were no dogs. So what can I say? And we had workers, the night crew, say, "I'm not going back there to wash the bus. I can't stand the dogs barking back there." But there were no dogs. And that's the way it was.

I guess I've been through a lot of things. I was raised up in that area. I went to Pu'uhale School, Kalākaua Intermediate, and Farrington High School, so I went through a lot of things over there. As the years go by I can think way back about all these Hawaiian spooks.

I used to drive the tourists out to Lanikuhonua on O'ahu's leeward side. You know that's a very sacred place. That's where the queen and king used to go on vacation, and a lot of things still go on out there.

And anyway, when everybody got off the bus and went to the *lū'au*, I'd stay on the bus, take a nap and sometimes wake up because the bus would be rocking back and forth like somebody big, like a person, a big person, was walking on the bus. Nobody on the bus.

Sometimes, I would look in the back, see a big body, you know, a human, sitting in the back seat.

"Somebody there?"

No answer.

Aw, must be just a dream, or something.

So I'd go back to sleep again, and after awhile I could feel the bus moving again, like a big person was walking down and walking back up.

I saw a big shadow in the back of the bus. I flipped on the light and walked back there and there's nobody there. That happened about three, four times.

And it happened to our other driver too. Well, that driver's not alive anymore, but that's what happened. The bus would be rocking, somebody walking in the bus, and you look and nobody's there. Or you can see a big shadow, big, three-, four-hundred pounder. And the bus starts rocking.

Oh, shit! Okay, no more sitting on the bus. I go out with the gang.

Al Tolentino, born on O'ahu and raised in Kaka'ako, went to Puahale School, Kalākaua Intermediate, and Farrington High School. He drove a tour bus, joined the U.S. Army, served in Europe and Asia, and survived three combat tours in Vietnam, where he encountered Agent Orange. Tolentino now tells his stories at Honolulu International Airport, where he operates Al's Shoe Shine.

Pele

Sometimes it's no big thing to drive down Chain of Craters Road in Hawai'i Volcanoes National Park to see the work of Madame Pele. Other times, it's a real nightmare, as Michael Dalke explains in his story about the night he and three pals got . . .

No Sleep in Pele's World

We all know never never take any volcanic rocks. We all know the wrath of Madame Pele. These are things we know. Well, I was involved in an incident that became kind of a nightmare, all because a guy with me actually did that, took rocks from Madame Pele's world.

It happened four or five years ago. We were in Hilo, negotiating a timber deal, and two people with me weren't from Hawai'i. They heard about the volcano. It was going off at the moment, so that evening we said let's drive down and take a look.

We drove to Volcano, had a few drinks at the Volcano House, and then headed down Chain of Craters Road, watching the glow all the way. It was very bright and beautiful, and we were excited to walk in and see the volcano. We came around a corner and—bammmmm! It sounded like we ran over a huge boulder.

What the hell was that? We all got out of the car, looked around the car, looked under the car, no flat tire, no boulders, no evident problem, the suspension was intact, all four tires good. We saw nothing. We all got back in the car and kept going.

Thirty minutes later, by the time we got down to the

end of Chain of Craters Road where the lava runs across the road, plenty of people had already walked in, so we had to turn around at the end of the road and come back to find a parking spot.

We parked, got out, and headed down the road toward the new lava flow. That's when we noticed a pool of oil at the place where you turn around, and we thought, oh, some poor guy is losing oil.

We walked about an hour, got closer to the lava flow, didn't get all the way to see it. It's tough going in the dark across the *pāhoehoe* with only a flashlight, light bobbing, ground uneven, real dark. And we got tired, didn't get close enough to see the lava boiling into the ocean, so we turned around and came back to the car. It was about two in the morning.

Again, we saw the oil pool, and we started laughing at the poor guy who lost his oil, and as we walked toward our car we noticed the oil slick kept going and it went right under our rental car.

Oh, no, we must have hit something up on the road.

One fellow who was with us has car dealerships and knew what to look at under the hood and under the chassis and he found a big hole in the pan. Not one drop of oil left. We pretty well knew if we drove up the hill we'd blow up the rental car. It wouldn't be a good thing.

We decided to just crash there for the night. No one was going anywhere. We couldn't see anybody. It was pitch dark, no stars, just the eerie red glow of the volcano.

About an hour later, a family came back from the lava, and they were going back up, offered a ride. I said, you guys stay here, I'll go back with them and call a tow truck. Nothing to it. They gave me a ride to Volcano House. That was about three o'clock.

I called Hilo, a tow truck came out, I gave him directions, he went down and got the car, got the other two guys, came back to pick me up at Volcano House. So we're all together again, start climbing into the cab of the tow truck and the driver says, "Not! Cannot! Can only have three in the front seat."

So I had to rent a room for one of the guys, put him up at Volcano House, and the three of us drove back to Hilo, the driver dropped the rental car, dropped us at the Naniloa.

We got two hours sleep. Up again. Called the rental company. Got another car. I raced up to Volcano House to pick up the other guy to drive him back to the next meeting in Hilo.

We got back to Volcano House. Harry was deathly ill in the hotel. He was like white, couldn't go to the meeting. He lay in bed all day. We had the meeting, came back, he was still real sick, so sick he couldn't travel. I noticed three lava rocks sitting on the bed and I said, "Harry, what the hell is that?"

He had done the absolute tabu and picked up rocks in the lava field, and Madame Pele was doing her number on him.

We got him together and caught a five o'clock plane back to O'ahu and put him to bed. Next morning he went to the doctor. We mailed the rocks back to the postmaster in Volcano. And three or four days later he was feeling a little bit better but still pretty junk.

He did finally recover. We never did get to see the lava. We never closed the timber deal. All of it, I guess, was not meant to be. I'll never again take anyone to see the volcano who isn't from Hawai'i.

Michael Dalke is a designer of tropical-style homes and furnishings in Hawai'i and the Pacific. He's created furniture for Pier One, designed Beverly Hills boutiques and Las Vegas casinos. Two decades ago Dalke came to Hawai'i and began exploring appropriate shelter for the tropics. He pioneered the use of *bangkiri*, a termite-proof Indonesian hardwood that resembles teak. His work includes houses in Lanikai, Waikāne, the Big Island of Hawai'i, Kaua'i, and resorts in the far Pacific. He lives in Ka'a'awa on O'ahu's windward side.

When you go to the Big Island of Hawai'i you may meet an old lady with a young face and long, white hair. Kalina Chang did when she went for a walk in North Kohala and took . . .

A Lady's Advice

My cousin and her husband were attending a seminar on the Big Island, so my husband and I went over to join them for a couple of days. Having some free time, we went up to the North Kohala area. I had been to many places on the Big Island, but had never been to that part before.

We parked on a *pali*, and down below was a black sand beach. There was a trail, and my cousin and her husband wanted to hike down to the beach, so off they went. Not knowing we might do this, I was wearing slippers. My husband didn't feel like hiking, so he was sitting in the car, relaxing.

I wondered if the trail was easy enough to try, wearing slippers. I turned around and there she was: a lady sitting on the rock wall. Her hair was long and white-gray, but her face was young. She smiled and said hello. I told her I was thinking of going down the trail to join my cousin, but didn't know if I could do that with what I was wearing on my feet. Or could I go barefoot?

She said she knew the trail well, and I definitely should go, and wear the slippers because there were some rocks. After I walked to the trailhead, a few feet away, I decided to thank her for the advice. But when I turned around, she was gone. I went on down the trail; in some places it was rocky, but nothing serious.

Later, I asked my husband if he saw the woman. He said he saw her sitting on the rock wall. I asked if he saw her arrive, and he said, "No." Then I asked if he saw her leave, and he said, "No."

That day my cousin decided to take some black sand home with her to California, as she likes to collect small amounts of sand from everywhere. She also took a few rocks from down on the Kohala Coast, though she knew she wasn't supposed to.

Two weeks later she called me. She had boxed up the rocks and was sending them to me to take back to Kohala. Their dog had become extremely sick, and her husband also had some health problems.

I thought about the lady on the wall with her long white hair. Did she encourage me to join them hoping I would be able to persuade them not to take anything? I guess I will always wonder about her.

Kalina Chang is a graphic artist who lives in windward Oʻahu. She paddles with Keahiakahoe Canoe Club, in Kahaluʻu, and enjoys writing and crafts. She is currently editing and doing cover art for a mainland author.

Now and then bones
surface in Waikīkī. A ghost
haunts the ʻIlikai, I am told,
although I never found
an eyewitness.
I once read that Jane
Stanford, who died of
poisoning at the Moana,
still haunts the halls.
Again, no eyewitness.
If ghosts haunt Waikīkī,
I guess folks just don't like
to talk about it, afraid to
scare the tourists. But the
other day I met David
Soares, who told me
about the time . . .

Madame Pele Visited Waikīkī

Years ago, when I worked for the Hilton Hawaiian Village for six weeks in housekeeping, the maids were afraid to walk down the hallways. This was in 1958, when they made the movie *South Pacific*, and I met Mitzi Gaynor and Rosanno Brazzi.

On certain nights, the maids used to see Pele down in the hallways wearing a red *muʻumuʻu*. They all were afraid to walk down the hallways at a certain hour. I was the only one who dared to walk down the hallways.

Mitzi Gaynor and Rosanno Brazzi had a big party to celebrate the end of shooting of *South Pacific* on Kauaʻi. So the head housekeeper set up for the party in the hallway. When I walked in at that hour the Hawaiians and Filipinos were going around the hallways and up the stairways to avoid running into Pele.

I never did encounter Madame Pele, never had what you'd call an introduction, but Pele seemed to be very much alive and real to those who saw her. She used to appear regularly at the Hilton Hawaiian Village, but some said it was just the ghost of a woman who died there. I don't know. That was an old burial ground, back in the 1700s. This is the word handed down by generations.

I'll be sixty-five this year, and almost fully alert, and a real *kolohe*, Hawaiian rascal, but I never did see Madame Pele there, but I saw the fear on the faces of the people who did.

Me? I was never afraid. When I was a little boy my father told me, "Only fear a living soul. The dead ones can't hurt you." Isn't that true?

David Soares, born in Honolulu, grew up on a Big Island ranch. He returned to O'ahu, where he worked for Chevron USA until his retirement. He and his wife, Angeline, live in Kukui Gardens. He is active in Honolulu Police Department's "Weed and Seed" youth program, St. Louis Alumni Association, and Notre Dame Alumni Club of Hawai'i.

A Honolulu journalist sets
out to investigate the myth
of Madame Pele's curse and
uncovers true-life cases
of bad luck caused by the
fire goddess. Some may
scoff and say it's a
coincidence, but just in case
it's not, I think it's probably
a good idea to . . .

Leave the Rocks Alone

A curse made up by a park ranger fifty-five years ago in an effort to stop visitors from collecting lava rocks is causing havoc over the power of these stones. Because of the superstitious belief that Madame Pele will inflict suffering on those who take her lava, the goddess of the volcano has been blamed for countless calamities.

That's why the staff at Hawai'i Volcanoes National Park doesn't want another story written about lava rocks. They say that each article generates even more returns of lava rocks to the park. Norrie Judd, one of the park's rangers, receives about five packages a day from visitors wanting to return something they took from the islands. A majority of the items sent back are lava rocks, but sand, coral, figurines and jewelry made out of lava are also common.

"People sent them back for a reason. They have very sad stories," she says. "Their house was broken into, they broke their leg, somebody died. Then they hear about this curse of taking things off the island and they send it back with their humble apology in hopes that the curse is broken."

Judd does not believe in Pele's curse, and wishes

people would stop sending the rocks back.

"We have not found any written curse in the history associated with lava rocks. It's very time-consuming to open the boxes and read the letters and put the rocks back," Judd complains.

In fact, it takes up so much of her time that she can no longer do it and has passed the job on to volunteers.

"Like any other national park in the country, it [Hawai'i Volcanoes] is protected by law, and you don't take things from it. And if everybody was just doing what they are supposed to be doing, we wouldn't be getting all these rocks," Judd says.

But for Patti Lee, a geology instructor at the University of Hawai'i, collecting lava rocks is part of her job. She hears the stories about people's misfortunes and the possible connection with Pele. In fact, she receives packages of lava rocks as well. And like Judd, she doesn't believe in the curse, but believes it's just a coincidence.

"They're looking for an excuse for their bad luck," she explains.

Lee collects her rocks from the Big Island, but not from Kīlauea. And in her thirteen years at UH, she says she has never experienced anything bad that she might blame on the rocks. Maybe it's because she uses them for educational purposes rather than for personal ones.

But there is one change she's noticed over the years: "The only thing that happens is that my husband's arms get longer and longer from bringing all these rocks home for me," Lee laughs.

Not everyone, however, agrees that the myth is just a hoax. Jon Osorio, a UH Hawaiian Studies professor, believes there is a possible link between people's bad experiences and Pele.

"For Hawaiians, there is a long tradition that you don't take things that don't belong to you," Osorio explains. "What it comes down to is a matter of respect."

Lava rocks are a *kinolau* (form) of Pele. And although some people see the *pōhaku* as just another rock, it is actually considered a valuable resource to Hawaiians.

"The rocks are there for the community," Osorio says. "To take them, you're stealing from the community."

And there are many phenomenal stories that have people thinking twice about stealing from Pele.

Crew members aboard a Hawaiian Airlines flight last year say that after takeoff, the pilot returned to the airport because of possible mechanical problems. While engineers examined the plane, a passenger handed over a lava rock to an airline employee. Engineers found nothing wrong with the plane, and the flight took off again— this time with no reason for the pilot to return.

Although nobody knows for sure if this incident was of Pele's doing, Osorio says he wouldn't be surprised if it was: "It's possible that there are lots of people taking lava rocks who have not had anything happen to them. In this particular case, that was probably Pele acting up, but what was so significant about this rock, I don't know."

On the other hand, musician Stephen Brown is positive about his encounter with Pele during his trip to the Big Island twenty-three years ago.

He came with his cousin who was moving to Kona. Their first stop was Hōnaunau, also known as the City of

Refuge. While there, Brown picked up two perfect hula stones. Almost immediately strange things began to happen.

"First, the car overheated. Then my cousin's friend cut his foot while walking on some lava rocks," he remembers.

But that had no effect on Brown who, at their next stop, picked up a couple more rocks near the Kalapana lava flow to add to his collection. But this time, Pele made sure she would get his attention.

"All of a sudden, everything changed. My cousin and his girlfriend, who I have never seen argue, are at each other's throats. No one's enjoying themselves. My cousin's girlfriend takes off on her own and he chases after her. Then some guy comes and picks a fight with us at the car," Brown recalls. The two got back in the car and, after an unsuccessful search for the couple, they called it a night.

"It's about 2 A.M. and we decide to take the shortcut back to Kona. We're going up Saddle Road and there's a lot of turns and pretty much when the curves stop you're on top, between the two volcanoes," Brown remembers. "Then—right when it starts to straighten out—we see this figure of a person walking on the road. The person is not getting any closer as we're driving and we're thinking it's very strange. All of a sudden it looks like she's right in front of us and we screech [the brakes] and look. But we don't see her, and then we see her and then we don't see her. Next thing we know our car konks out."

After letting the car sit awhile, the two men successfully started the car again and, luckily, no more bizarre things happened. Brown returned home to Kuliou'ou the next day, but he did not yet escape the curse. The next morning he awoke very weak. He couldn't lift his arms or legs and had a hard time talking. His sister walked up to him and gave him a weird look.

"She grabs the mirror and there's, like, a golf-ball–sized lump on my neck," Brown explains.

Doctors at the hospital emergency room couldn't tell him what it was either. He called his mom on the Big Island.

"I told her something's wrong and the first thing she said was, 'What did you take from the Big Island?' "

She returned his rock collection, and once that happened—surprise!—the lump on Brown's neck disappeared. But he still bears a memory of Pele, a scar on his right hand from the fight with the stranger that eerie night in the car.

Whether Pele's curse is real or not, there is one thing on which believers and nonbelievers both agree: Leave the rocks alone.

Yu Shing Ting is a staff writer for *MidWeek*, where this article first appeared. A journalism graduate of the University of Hawai'i, she served as news editor and managing editor of *Ka Leo O Hawaii*, the UH daily newspaper. She enjoys running and playing basketball.

M any people, misinformed people, think Haleakalā crater is extinct, but that's not true. The crater is only dormant, which means it's still very much alive and way overdue to go off again. Somewhere deep down in the volcanic heart of Maui, the pot still boils and the geologic clock is ticking, something to consider when you . . .

Ride to the Source

Our horse's forelocks are wrapped in cowhide to guard against the razor's edge of lava. Slowly, we pick our way around jagged shards of *'a'ā*. If we spill in this *terra terrabilis* we surely will be slashed to shreds.

I lean far forward in my saddle as we head from Mākena up the south side of Haleakalā on Maui's 'Ulupalakua Ranch, a vertical spread on a nearly two-mile-high volcano that's not done yet.

This old volcano is officially classified as dormant, which means it can go off at any moment. Not today, we hope.

We are riding to the source, to Pu'u Māhoe, the last lava flow from Haleakalā crater that went off about 1780, the last time Maui experienced a volcanic eruption.

In the deep time of geology that's only yesterday. Perouse, the first white man to set foot on Maui, on May 29, 1786, described "a shore made hideous by an ancient lava flow," and sailed on, never to be seen again, yet another mystery of the Pacific.

The lava reflects the sun's heat deep into my bones. I am glad to have an old *lauhala* hat on my head and water in my saddlebag.

No one knows exactly when Haleakalā last erupted, but everyone knows it is long overdue. I wonder when it will roar again.

The thought of eruption is very much on my mind as we ride to the last crater that erupted on Maui.

We ride by *kiawe* with stiletto thorns that can pierce a leather boot, past old, sun-bleached bones (whose? I wonder), across wide stretches of nothing but lava that once was alive and dribbling down to the shore.

Nothing stirs in this dead zone except fine clouds of suffocating red dust kicked up by our horses. I pull a red bandanna across my face as we ride on deeper into Pele land.

We rein in at the source: a classic cone crater with a tell-tale tongue of *pāhoehoe* sticking out its downhill lip.

I walk to the edge and look down the throat of this old crater's hell-hole and see only dead ashes. Way down there somewhere, I know, the pot still boils.

From the crater to the sea, Maui looks like an eighteenth-century engraving of itself, an island frozen in time, smothered by miles of lava in every direction as far as the eye can see, a black silent place, Pele's world.

Out of the sun-struck sea a whale leaps, my horse flicks its tail, and in that very moment, standing there on the dormant crater, Maui seems to exist only in the primeval. I am glad to head on down the narrow trail and return to the present.

Author and photojournalist Rick Carroll is the collector of the six books of stories in the *Hawai'i's Best Spooky Tales* series. His latest book, *Huahine: Island of the Lost Canoe*, is a true-life archaeological mystery set in the Society Islands.

Faces

....

Something's in the Picture

The Hitchhiker of Laupāhoehoe

Tūtū Lady's Taro Patch

When the gang went in search of fun in Honolulu one night they took a camera to record their diversions. They bought a pair of devil's horns at the Waimānalo Carnival and took turns taking pictures of each other. That's when a strange thing began to occur, which they can prove because . . .

Something's in the Picture

One Friday night a bunch of friends and I decided to spend a night out on the town—goof around, hang out, just get out of the house and away from computers. The four of us (Debbie, Patrick, Thomas, and I) all hopped in my car and went out for an evening of adventure; little did we know that this evening was one we'd not forget for a long time.

We set off to Waimānalo Carnival about ten o'clock. When we got to the carnival we found that it was a bit crowded and not much was amusing. If anything, what amused us was the blinking devil horns we saw on this one guy there. We made our rounds, and Debbie, Patrick, and Thomas decided the horns were much more fitting for me. Debbie went ahead and bought a pair.

Once we got 'em, we decided to head out for some grinds at Byron's by the airport. After our order was complete, we headed out for a little surprise we had in store for Patrick, an airplane lover. We decided to go hang out by the parking lot down by Lagoon Drive in the far back.

When we approached the area it was coned off. Well, being the motivated people we were, we noticed a space between the cones that was big enough for my car. Yup, we drove on through! Figured no biggie. I mean what was the harm? All we were gonna do was have our dinner in the parking lot and watch planes land and take off. No crime there, right?

Anyhow, right away we all dug into our plates and ate up a hearty meal. Just so happened I brought along my new Sony Mavica digital camera that I hadn't used yet; I figured, a night out with three loony friends, there's bound to be a Kodak moment, know what I mean?

So after the meal we messed around taking turns posing with the horns we got from the carnival. I already got my pic taken with them back in Waimānalo, and now it was everyone else's turn. Thomas went first. We put some music on, and Thomas started dancin' and having a grand old time. Laughing and encouraging, we snapped a few, decided which were funny enough to keep. Then it was Debbie's turn.

We all cheered her on when she climbed the light pole and posed for a pic. We all joked that even though she had horns on she looked like a happy devil. The fact that the camera caused a lot of "red eye" pics was kinda cool, 'cause it went with the theme of the horns and all.

Last, it was Patrick's turn. Thomas was snapping at this time and set up a pose in which Patrick was flexing. At the very last minute I shouted out to Patrick to make some funny faces. The flash went off, and all I can remember is Thomas's face. He turned pale in an instant and shook his head and we rushed over to see the pic. At first glance, I felt something was terribly wrong. I hoped it was a glare of sorts, but in my gut I knew it wasn't.

Something was in the picture. And it wasn't one of us.

Thomas said out loud, "This isn't good." Debbie walked over, looked at the pic and we all agreed, "Holy shit!" Patrick looked stunned—damn, we all were. Not even three seconds later we all were in the car ready to get the hell outta there. Patrick, who was in the passenger seat, let out the hand brake before I even started the car.

We drove off pretty damn quick, looking back at the pic that was stored on the camera. I pulled into a gas station and we all kinda crawled over each other to get another glance at this very odd picture. We gassed up the car and left. Destination at that time was completely unknown. We drove for a few minutes, still in awe. Debbie broke into chicken skin, and Patrick involuntarily shed a tear. Thomas was quiet, which is rare, and I tried to make light of the situation by joking. It didn't work.

I suggested we go to our usual hangout behind the 'Ilikai Hotel in Waikīkī, which we've affectionately come to call "Canoes." We pulled in, got out of the car and decided that it had to be a lighting issue. I mean Patrick had on a white shirt, there was a flash, and there was a big street lamp behind Thomas. One of those must have been a factor—so we tried to believe. We thought that if we recreated the lighting scenario maybe we could really confirm if it was lighting or glare.

Patrick and Debbie took a pic together. Nothing. Jus' Debbie, jus' Thomas, jus' me, all okay. Then Thomas took one of Patrick by the canoes, and again Thomas's face dropped. There was a small visible "something" in the pic. So we said, okay, try another one. We all tried to snap a photo. Never failed. The only time it showed up was a) when Thomas was the photographer, and b) Patrick was the one being photographed.

This was starting to get downright eerie. So Thomas tried a different position. He snapped and almost dropped the camera as he passed it to me and walked off. I looked at it, Patrick came running over, Debbie leered over my shoulder.

This time the "something" was much more visible. The camera, which had been freshly charged earlier that evening, told us we had a few more minutes left on the battery charge. So we snapped away trying to get "it" again.

Nothing. Every time after that last pic that was so strong, stronger than the one at the airport, no more pics came out like the other three. So we took a few of all of us. Me, Patrick, Debbie. Debbie, Patrick, and Thomas. I figured I could use Photoshop to paste someone into whichever one came out better. Still nothing. We were befuddled to say the least. Had not a clue what it was, or why it was there.

Now all of us being raised here in Hawai'i, we know a little folklore and what "felt" right and what didn't. I mean almost every local kid knows that "no pork over the Pali" kinda thing.

Well, we all just kinda sat at the table and talked very little. I knew what was on the mind of each and every one of us. Thomas seemed to wonder why only the photos he took of Patrick came out that way. Of course Patrick wondered why only his pics came out like that as well. Debbie and I joked about being happy that it wasn't our pics.

Not at just one place, but at two entirely different locations, anomalies showed in photos—photos that had only two things in common: Patrick and Thomas. What was the connection, if any? It was about 2 A.M., and we decided to head on out to Kailua to drop Debbie off at home. The ride was extremely quiet.

After Debbie, it was Thomas in Salt Lake, then Patrick in 'Ewa Beach. We talked some, but were still baffled by the night's occurrences. We were anxious to see how the pics would look on the computer. Would it show up there? Would we get a clearer picture of what was there? Did we want to know?

I finally made my way back to Wai'anae at nearly 3:30 A.M. I instantly threw the diskette in the computer, and the others were at home waiting online for the results. The pics looked even more eerie in full size.

A day or so passed and we each came up with theories of our own. Patrick at first was convinced it was glare, lighting, and his shirt. Thomas was convinced from the get-go that it was an *'uhane* (spirit), sharing its presence with us. Debbie shared the pics and story with her boyfriend, and he suggested cigarette smoke. We thought about it and, yeah, that was it! It had to be it!

But Thomas wasn't smoking when he took these pics. I think in a small way Debbie and I were disappointed. We wanted to believe it was something logical, something that could be explained beyond a reasonable doubt.

So I went back to my original idea that it was Patrick's recently deceased aunt, who was looking over him. Patrick didn't really seem to buy it. Ever since then, we all have our own ideas I'm sure. We all looked online to see photos with characteristics like ours. We found some that looked pretty damn authentic and some that were blatantly touched-up. We discussed possibly returning to the site at the airport to confirm the lighting and reenact the photo. Patrick and Debbie were quite clear that they weren't gonna participate, and I don't really blame them. Thomas wanted to do it. I didn't really care one way or another.

We threw around the idea of taking the pic to a famous psychic in Kāhala named Lon Vo. Still contemplating it. Each of us have shown the pics to people we know and have gotten different feedback. The most frequent opinion was that something indeed accompanied us on our little venture that night. It could be? We may never know.

I put this story and pics on my site to perhaps catch the eye of someone who could shed some light on the situation. I strongly encourage any or all for feedback, opinions, sarcasm, or anything—something. That night has been on the minds of all four of us and I know I speak for them all when I say that an explanation would be nice. Was it cigarette smoke? Patrick's aunt? Glare? Or was someone truly there with the four of us that night? You be the judge.

Born and raised on the west coast of Oʻahu in Waiʻanae, Healani Ortiz was educated in the Hawaiian ways by her grandmother Addie Kalanikalokomaikaʻinui Naʻiwi from early on, and lives with the belief that until Hawaiʻi's supernatural touches your life, you will never fully respect the phenomenal nature of Hawaiʻi. Healani now lives in Honolulu working as a webmaster for an ISP. She and her fiancé are also the owners of a commercial web design company, CODA Studios. To see photos of the "something," visit her Web site:
www.wahineonline.com/torf.html

You never know who or what you may encounter when you stop to give a hitchhiker a ride on the Big Island of Hawai'i, especially if the hour is late and the road to Hilo town is dark, and you are the only soul on the highway. Cheryl Duarte takes us for a chilling ride in this unusual spooky tale about . . .

The Hitchhiker of Laupāhoehoe

On a crisp and clear morning, shortly past the midnight hour, a young man in his twenties travels alone along the dark stretch of the road leading to Hilo town on the Big Island of Hawai'i. As he passes Laupāhoehoe he sees a figure in the distance that appears to be hitchhiking along the side of the deserted highway.

Upon nearing the figure he realizes that it is a woman dressed entirely in black. She wears a long hooded coat and long black gloves. Feeling she is in distress, he pulls over and offers her a ride. She graciously accepts.

The dark of the early morning sky doesn't enable the young man to get a close look at her, but trusting that she is harmless, he continues along. After having traveled awhile in complete silence, the driver tries in vain to make conversation with his passenger.

Deciding she has probably fallen asleep, curiosity overwhelms him and he wants to catch a glimpse of the quiet stranger. Not wanting to take his eyes off the road for too long, he cautiously leans forward and is unprepared for what he finds: nothing but darkness peering out from behind her hooded cloak.

Beginning to worry and unsure of what is taking

place, he glances down at the rest of her and realizes she doesn't have any feet.

Panic-stricken, he yanks the vehicle over and rushes off to find a pay phone. Upon returning to the car, he finds she has disappeared.

Feeling vulnerable and frightened, he decides it would be better to drive the rest of the way home than to stay in the middle of nowhere, alone, until the morning comes. In shock, he gets back into his car and forces himself to continue. Inside the car he finds himself shivering and rolls up the windows to keep warm. Funny, he thinks to himself, that he hadn't noticed how cold it was outside. But the inside of the car continues to get colder even with the windows rolled up.

Unable to keep his mind off of the ghostly passenger, he glances down to where she once sat. In her place remains an indentation, as if someone is still sitting next to him.

Cheryl Duarte has a B.A. degree in journalism from the University of Hawai'i. Married, she currently lives in windward O'ahu and enjoys reading, spending time with family and friends, and writing poetry. Cheryl says, "This actually happened to my brother-in-law, Keola. He lived in Kona, but used to travel to Hilo often to visit his friends."

Sometimes when you
are told not to look in a
forbidden place and
curiosity gets the best
of you, you may
be in for a surprise,
as Margo Howlett was
on her visit to . . .

Tūtū *Lady's* *Taro Patch*

We grew up in Lāʻie, right next to the graveyard, and that was a spooky time because my uncle and others used to tell stories to all us kids about the night marchers and wandering spirits and *akua lele* (fireballs) flying around, and we were always warned to make sure we were in the house when it got dark.

Across the street was Lāʻie Park, and past Lāʻie Park, toward the mountains, was our favorite spot to play, *tūtū* lady's taro patch. *Tūtū* lady's taro patch became our family pool, because once she farmed the taro, water gushed in, and we—my brothers and sisters and I—liked to go there and spend our days. I was a little girl, maybe five or six.

We were always going up to the mountains to pick mangos or plums or ginger and figs, always something we could eat. Anyway, there was a shack next to the taro patch. It wasn't big and it didn't have windows, just a door. We were always told, "Don't look in the keyhole." So, of course, we all wanted to look in the keyhole. But every time someone would try to peep in there, someone would come and scare them from behind.

One day my sister, Janice, remembered her *tūtū's*

birthday was the next day, and she wanted to pick ginger, make a *lei*. So, in *tūtū* lady's taro patch is a lot of ginger. My sister's asking everyone to go there with her, but it was in the evening already, maybe five-thirty, quarter to six.

When she asked my brother, Jimmy, he said, "Janice, don't you know tonight is *pōkane* night when the night marchers come out?"

"Please," she begged, "you guys come with me. If we all go we can pick it real fast and be out of there before it's dark."

And Jimmy said, "No way!" Janice went down the line and everybody said, "No way! You're crazy!"

Since I was the youngest, she looked at me and said, "You're going with me." And she just pulled me by my hair and dragged me to the taro patch. I had no choice, and I remember screaming the whole way over there.

Once we got there I was calm because the taro patch is so beautiful and fun. I was just sitting on the side of the taro patch while she was picking her ginger. Now there were a lot of things racing through my mind, and the main thing was to hurry up and get out of there before it got dark because that's when the night marchers come out, right at dusk.

Janice was busy picking her ginger, and I was sitting down, and all of a sudden I got chicken skin. My whole body was covered with chicken skin. I looked around and I knew it was getting dark soon and I was scared. So I just kept wishing that my sister would hurry up and pick her ginger so we could get out of there.

While I was looking around, I saw the shack out of

the corner of my eye. I got chicken skin again and I was so scared. I looked at the shack and I said to myself, "Gee, I wonder if this is a good time to look through the keyhole." I looked over to my sister to see if she was far away enough from me that she couldn't scare me if I looked through the keyhole. She was busy, picking her ginger. She was singing and humming, so I got up enough nerve and started walking to that shack.

When I got there, I leaned down and I went for the keyhole—and I changed my mind. But I really wanted to take a look. So, I got up my nerve again, and when I looked in that keyhole I saw a woman sitting on a chair brushing her hair. When she stood up her hair fell down behind her and touched the floor.

Her hair was so long and so beautiful, I went, "Ooooh," and when I did that she turned around and looked to the door and she had no face, no face at all. All she had was like a round blank, just bone and skin, not even sockets for her eyeballs, not a bump for a nose, no mouth. I screamed and ran away and I fell down and got myself up again and kept running.

My sister, who was busy picking her ginger, looked up and said, "Eh, wassamattah you?" and I just went, "Aaaaaaah!" and kept running out of there.

"Margo, where are you going?" she called.

"I saw the lady in the shack!"

"What are you talking about?"

"I saw the lady in the shack!"

"Get over here. I'm not finished."

"She has no face!"

"What?"

"The lady in the shack has no face!"

That's when I heard her fall—splat—into the water. I looked at her and kept screaming and running.

"Margo, wait for me!"

I just kept on running. She came out of the water and dropped all her ginger, started running after me. "You, wait for me."

We both ran.

"I saw the lady, and she had no face!"

"You liar."

"You go look."

"Hell, no," she said.

As we were running back, a lot of people living on that street came out of their houses, wondering what we were screaming about. We looked at each other and screamed and kept running until we got home.

We told our brothers about it and they didn't believe us, and we challenged them to go back but they never did. But I saw the lady with no face.

Anyway, a couple of years later, I remember my sister telling me there was talk on the radio and stories in the Honolulu newspapers about there being a woman people had seen in public restrooms around the island. And they said she had no face. She was seen a lot at the Waialae Theater restrooms, but after they broke that down she was sighted at Nānākuli restrooms and many other public restrooms.

Margo Howlett was born and raised in Lā'ie, where four or five generations of her family also grew up. Her story "The Good News Dog" appeared in *Hawai'i's Best Spooky Tales 4*.

Aloha

....

The Last Aloha *and Farewell*

Drums in the Night

People who live in Hawai'i
are not so very eager to
leave. And who can blame
them? Everyone knows
Hawai'i is a kind of paradise
on Earth. Two loved ones
decide to take one last look
around before bidding . . .

The Last Aloha and Farewell

Recently I was throwing out some college papers and found one I wrote in English 101 class at Leeward Community College back in 1982 on extrasensory perception. It was a story about the time my husband, Sonny, saw a ghost.

Our old neighbors Roger and Gail were always visiting Washington State because of Gail's widowed mother. They made numerous trips to and from Hawai'i. Roger always asked Sonny if he would keep an eye on the house, water the plants, and make sure everything was okay while they were gone.

One time, while Roger and Gail were gone, Sonny saw Roger's father in the house. He had met Roger's father before and was startled to see him standing there at the top of the staircase. "He stood quietly, as if inspecting every corner of the house and reminiscing some good times spent there," Sonny recalled. "He didn't acknowledge me as I waved and said, 'Hi, didn't know you were supposed to be here.' "

When Sonny told Roger about seeing his father, Roger reacted with great surprise. "It can't be so. No relative would bring him here, because he is seriously ill and near death." After his father died, Roger and Gail sold their house in Waipahu and moved to Washington.

The incident reminded me of the time with my mother. She was in her last stage of cancer. One day, she desperately wanted my father to drive her to my sister Pat's house by the lake. Knowing no one was home, my father reluctantly drove her there. He later said he couldn't understand why she wanted to go there, because she was almost completely blind.

I believe it was my mother's last farewell to the home where she enjoyed the fun and laughter of her first two grandchildren and all the other members of the family. For the last time, she wanted to feel the cool breeze that swayed the huge trees along Wahiāwa's Lake Wilson.

Was it an out-of-body spirit that Sonny encountered that day at Roger's house? I think Roger's father and my mother, both gravely ill, each wanted to take a final look at this life and convey their love and *aloha* for the last time before crossing over.

Gloriana C. Valera grew up on pineapple plantations on Moloka'i and O'ahu. A graduate of Leilehua High School and Kapiolani Technical School of Business (now Kapi'olani Community College), she is retired after a career as a secretary-steno at Hickam Air Force Base. She and her husband, also retired (from the Air National Guard and from running—three Honolulu Marathons), enjoy babysitting their grandchildren and helping relatives or neighbors who need emergency babysitting. Her story "Pat and Me" appeared in *Hawai'i's Best Spooky Tales 4*.

The day Iz died
the people of Hawai'i
were grief-stricken.
Some said a prayer, others
wept. One woman, home
alone after dark, heard the
unmistakable sound of . . .

Drums in the Night

It started out as a morning like any other. I got up around six or so and turned on the radio. It then became a morning like no other. The news reporter said, "We are sorry to report the death of singer Israel Kamakawiwoʻole . . . ." My eyes filled with tears as I stood there, not wanting to believe what I heard. How could our "Hawaiian Sup'pa Man" suddenly be gone? Anyone who listened to Hawaiian music was aware of his health problems, but somehow we just weren't expecting him to die, not now, so young.

People, most of them choked up, began calling in to Hawaiian 105. Other stations were getting calls as well. KINE put through a call to the Makaha Sons, who were in Las Vegas at the time. Their shock and sadness reflected the reactions here as they grieved for the loss of their friend and former band member. Throughout the day, IZ's music was played across the Islands.

The following evening I was home alone, my husband at work on swing shift. We are in the last house on the road, next to the jungle at the foot of the Koʻolau Mountains. The windows and sliding door are nearly always open. It was after seven, and dark at the time. It was quiet in the house, as I had turned off the radio. I thought I might watch TV, and picked up the newspaper listings.

That's when I heard the drums. They sounded clear and very close, like right outside. There were two sets of the same beats. I went out on the upstairs *lānai* and listened. I turned on the outside light. I saw nothing and heard nothing more. There is nothing out there but dense jungle. My backyard is not accessible from the road.

The next day IZ's music was still being played on the radio in heavy rotation, and I heard the song "E Ala E" (the original version).

I suddenly realized that the drumbeats in the beginning of the song were identical to the ones I heard the night before. There was no one home but me at the time, so no one else to testify to it. I hesitate to tell people—they usually think I was dreaming—but I assure you I was plenty awake.

So I wonder: Was this his way of reassuring me (and anyone in earshot) that he was still with us? I have heard others say that they still feel his presence, and I believe that this will always be so.

Eh, IZ, how we miss you.

Kalina Chang is a graphic artist who lives in windward Oʻahu. She paddles with Keahiakahoe Canoe Club, in Kahaluʻu, and enjoys writing and crafts. She is currently editing and doing cover art for a mainland author.